LIFE NATURE LIBRARY

EVOLUTION

OTHER BOOKS
BY THE EDITORS OF LIFE

LIFE NATURE LIBRARY

EVOLUTION

by Ruth Moore
and The Editors of LIFE

TIME INCORPORATED
NEW YORK

A
STONEHENGE
BOOK

About the Author

Ruth Moore is a journalist who arrived at her interest in evolution in a roundabout way. For seven years she covered the Washington economic scene for the Chicago *Sun-Times*. One day, while she was attending an economics conference, a University of Chicago professor sitting next to her casually announced: "We're rewriting the theory of evolution." What the professor was referring to were some experiments in carbon-dating with fossils, and the new light they shed on the evolutionary time scale. Miss Moore began a series of articles about the experiments for the *Sun-Times*. The series led to a book, *Man, Time and Fossils*, which appeared in 1953 and has since been published in 10 languages. This success led in turn to other books on scientific subjects—*Charles Darwin: A Great Life in Brief* (1955), *The Earth We Live On* (1956) and *The Coil of Life* (1961). Today Miss Moore is one of the country's best-known and most respected writers of science for the general reader. She was born in St. Louis, Missouri, and attended Washington University from which she received her B.A. and M.A. degrees in economics and political science.

On the Cover

Red rock crabs and marine iguanas, sharing a wave-tossed rock in the Galápagos Islands, suggest a primeval scene. Darwin, who studied the primitive life of this "little world," gained insight here into evolution.

Contents

TIME-LIFE BOOKS

EDITOR
Norman P. Ross

TEXT DIRECTOR   ART DIRECTOR
William Jay Gold   Edward A. Hamilton

CHIEF OF RESEARCH
Beatrice T. Dobie

Assistant Text Director: Jerry Korn
Assistant Chief of Research: Monica O. Horne

•

PUBLISHER
Rhett Austell

General Manager: John A. Watters
Business Manager: John D. McSweeney
Circulation Manager: Joan D. Lanning

LIFE MAGAZINE

EDITOR: Edward K. Thompson
MANAGING EDITOR: George P. Hunt
PUBLISHER: Jerome S. Hardy

LIFE NATURE LIBRARY

Editorial Staff for *Evolution:*
EDITOR: Maitland A. Edey
Assistant to the Editor: George McCue
Copy Editor: Richard L. Williams
Designer: Paul Jensen
Staff Writers: David Bergamini, Dale Brown, Harvey B. Loomis, John MacDonald, Peter Meyerson
Chief Researcher: Martha Turner
Researchers: Doris Bry, Peggy Bushong, Joan Chasin, Eleanor Feltser, Le Clair G. Lambert, Paula Norworth, Roxanna Sayre, Paul W. Schwartz, Paul Trachtman, Phyllis M. Williamson, Sybil Wong
Picture Researchers: Margaret K. Goldsmith, Sue Bond, Mollie Cooper
Art Associate: Robert L. Young
Art Assistants: James D. Smith, Mark A. Binn
Copy Staff: Marian Gordon Goldman, Suzanne Seixas, Dolores A. Littles

The text for the chapters of this book was written by Ruth Moore, the picture essays were written by the editorial staff. The following individuals and departments of Time Incorporated were helpful in producing the book: Larry Burrows, John Dominis, Alfred Eisenstaedt, Eliot Elisofon, Robert W. Kelley, Nina Leen and Leonard McCombe, LIFE staff photographers; Howard Sochurek, LIFE contributing photographer; Doris O'Neil, Chief of the LIFE Picture Library; Richard M. Clurman, Chief of the TIME-LIFE News Service; and Content Peckham, Chief, Bureau of Editorial Reference.

Introduction

THERE has been a great change in the status of science within the last quarter century, and particularly since the Second World War. Science has become a source of power, not merely a subject fit for fiction. Scientific achievements loom ever larger in the competition for world prestige between the West and the East. Slowly it dawns on man in general that science is something of interest and concern not only to its dedicated practitioners but to himself as well. Mass media devote more and more space and time to scientific matters.

The achievement of science which has produced the greatest impression on mankind is the release of atomic energy. Regardless of what else it has done, the mushroom cloud which rose over the New Mexico desert in July 1945 has served to increase the popular appreciation of science. During this period—and since the industrial revolution began—the physical sciences have in general been in the forefront of the scientific movement. Man has exerted much greater efforts to control the forces of inanimate nature than to understand himself and the world of life of which he is a part. This situation is not, however, likely to endure much longer. It really begins to look as if the biological sciences are now surging ahead.

Of all the sciences, biology has the greatest relevance to the understanding of man. It was slightly more than a century ago, in 1859, that Darwin set forth the revolutionary idea which this book encompasses—that man, together with every other living thing, is a product of a process of evolutionary development. But man has not only evolved, he is still evolving. Human evolution is not all in the past, it is also an actuality and a concern for the future. The problem of possible genetic damage to human populations from radiation exposures, including those resulting from the fallout from testing of atomic weapons, has quite properly claimed much popular attention in recent years.

And yet this is only a part, and probably a relatively minor part, of the more serious and vastly greater problem of the maintenance of the genetic health of the human species. It is becoming more and more evident that man can no longer rely solely on Darwinian natural selection and other "natural" processes to insure his fitness to cope with the hazards of the environments in which he lives. Here mankind faces possibly the most portentous challenge of its whole history as a biological species. The time is not far off when man will have to regulate his numbers, and control his genetic patrimony in order to sustain his bodily and mental vigor. Knowledge and understanding are the prime requisites for a successful response to the great challenge, which is really a challenge to survival. To help people to acquire such knowledge and understanding is the aim of this book.

THEODOSIUS DOBZHANSKY
Professor
The Rockefeller Institute

1

Darwin's Voyage into the Past

A PECULIAR, pungent odor caught the attention of Charles Darwin as he walked through the lofty, sublime greenness of the Brazilian forest just outside Rio de Janeiro. The scent came from a curious fungus. The young naturalist quickly picked the mushroomlike plant, which reminded him of the familiar English Phallus. In autumn walks through the woods at home he had often seen beetles attracted to its noxious smell. Now, as he held the Brazilian Hymenophallus in his hand, a beetle swooped down and alighted upon it. The fungi were of different species; the beetles were of different species; yet in two distant countries they had developed the same relationship. A coincidence, perhaps, but Darwin could not help wondering about it.

The year was 1832 and he was 23, starting a five-year world cruise as the unpaid naturalist aboard H.M.S. *Beagle*—and finding the world full of coincidences, likenesses and differences that the prevailing theory of creation utterly failed to account for. The theory was both explicit and vague: every species of plant and animal on earth, it held, had come into being at one grand moment in time, presumably about 6,000 years ago, when "certain elemental atoms were suddenly commanded to flash into living tissues." But had beetles been created full-grown, or as larvae? Which had come first, the oak or the acorn, the pumpkin or the seed, the chicken or the egg? And why did many living species appear to be refinements of extinct, fossilized ones? The theory of spontaneous, special, separate creation did not say.

There were men who found the theory incredible, though Darwin was not yet one of them. For the present he was fully occupied with observing, collecting, comparing and wondering, and full of "a burning zeal to add even the most humble contribution to the noble structure of Natural Science." But his destiny was not humble but herculean: to jack up the whole noble structure and put a new foundation under it.

That foundation is evolution, the concept that there is a kinship among all forms of life because all evolved in an amplitude of time from one common ancestry, and that there are differences between them because they have diverged from that ancestry in taking over the earth, its air and its waters. Darwin did not invent the concept. But when he started his career, the doctrine of special creation could be doubted only by heretics. When he finished, the fact of evolution could be denied only by an abandonment of reason. He demolished the old theory with two books. One, published in 1859, he titled

ON THE ORIGIN OF SPECIES
by means of Natural Selection,
or the Preservation of Favoured Races
in the Struggle for Life.

The second, published in 1871, he called

THE DESCENT OF MAN,
and Selection in Relation to Sex.

The books did not so much undermine the old, comfortable order of things as simply overwhelm it; nobody had ever bothered to try documenting the other side—instantaneous creation—with such a painstakingly built structure of evidence. At two strokes Darwin gave modern science a rationale, a philosophy, an evolutionary, and thereby a revolutionary, way of thinking about the universe and everything in it, and incidentally established himself as the Newton of biology. But at the same time he dealt mankind's preening self-esteem a body blow from which it may never recover, and for which Darwin may never be quite forgiven. For it is one thing for man to be told (and want to believe) that he was created in the literal image of God. It is quite another thing for him to be told (and have to accept) that he is, while unique, merely the culmination of a billion years of ever-evolving life, and that he must trace his godhood down a gnarled and twisted family tree through mammals and amphibians to the lowly fish and thence to some anonymous, if miraculous, Adam molecule.

CHARLES ROBERT DARWIN was born February 12, 1809, the same day as Abraham Lincoln. He was the son of Dr. Robert Waring Darwin, a well-known physician, and the grandson of the even more noted Dr. Erasmus Darwin, physician, naturalist and, as a sometime poet, author of the *Zoonomia*. In that work Erasmus Darwin sought not only to unravel the theory of diseases, but also to explain life itself in evolutionary terms. "Would it be too bold," he asked, "to imagine that in the great length of time since the earth began to exist, perhaps millions of ages before the commencement of the history of mankind—would it be too bold to imagine that all warm-blooded animals have arisen from one

THALES

A Greek philosopher (640?-546 B.C.), Thales is conceded to be the first ancient thinker who applied scientific rather than mythological interpretations to the study of natural phenomena. He believed that all life originated in and arose out of water.

ARISTOTLE

A Greek naturalist and philosopher (384-322 B.C.), he collected and organized all the known zoological facts of his period. Aristotle made the first serious attempt to classify animals on the basis of their anatomy, probably from firsthand dissections.

living filament. . . ?" It was indeed too bold for the day—the *Zoonomia* was published in 1794. Although it was translated into several languages and attracted wide attention, its theory of life's origins was never taken seriously.

As Charles Darwin grew up in his father's large house, The Mount, near Shrewsbury, he often heard his grandfather's book discussed. Darwin's mother, Susannah Wedgwood Darwin, daughter of the great potter Josiah Wedgwood, had died when Charles was eight. Dr. Darwin liked to assemble his children and discourse at length and with authority on the views of his own father and a wide range of subjects. Young Charles listened with more awe than understanding. His father sternly disapproved not of his boyish pursuits—the collection of pebbles, insects, plants and birds' eggs—but of his poor record at the Shrewsbury Grammar School. The master, Samuel Butler, reported that Charles made little progress in Greek or Latin composition.

At 16 Charles was absorbed, as his father put it, in "shooting, dogs and rat-catching," and still was "doing no good" at school. Determined that his son should not grow up into an idle sportsman, Dr. Darwin sent Charles and his older brother Erasmus to the University of Edinburgh to study medicine. There Charles made a required visit to the operating theater. A child was being operated on, and chloroform and ether were not yet in use. Charles ran from the room, never to return. At about the same time, he learned that he would ultimately inherit enough property to live comfortably for all of his life. That ended his studies of medicine. When it became clear that Charles also had no inclination for the law, Dr. Darwin decreed that his son should become a clergyman. Always deferential and acquiescent to his redoubtable father—though seldom able to please him—Charles agreed. He could accept the creed of the Church of England and he liked the idea of a country church.

From 1828 to 1831 Charles was sent to Cambridge University to take the requisite degree. He did sufficient work with tutors to obtain respectable grades. The Cambridge he loved, though, was a different one—shooting small game with the sporting crowd, collecting beetles, walking with the Reverend John Stevens Henslow, professor of botany, and reading natural history. He was greatly stirred by Alexander von Humboldt's *Personal Narrative of Travels to the Equinoctial Regions of America during the Years 1799-1804*. He reread his grandfather. He also read Lamarck.

IN the early 1790s, while revolution roared through the streets of Paris, Jean-Baptiste Pierre Antoine de Monet, Chevalier de Lamarck, one of France's two professors of zoology, had undertaken a classification of all invertebrates. He soon saw that animals could be fitted into a stair-step series, a progression extending from the simplest little polyp at one end to man at the other.

"Citizens," wrote Lamarck, "go from the simplest to the most complex and you will have the true thread that connects all the productions of nature; you will have an accurate idea of her progression; you will be convinced that the simplest living things have given rise to all others." Animals, he thought, adapted to various environmental elements—climate, temperature, altitude—by using and developing the organs and characteristics best suited to their surroundings. And at the same time the ones they neglected to use proceeded to atrophy. In this way animals acquired special characteristics. And would not the handing-down of these acquired characteristics ultimately build up all the complexity of the living world? Even so had the giraffe acquired its long neck, the waterfowl their webbed feet, the elephant its massive body. Little objection

JEAN-BAPTISTE LAMARCK

He was a French naturalist and precursor (1744-1829) of Darwin. Lamarck also believed in evolutionary change, but thought such changes were brought on as an animal strove to adapt to its environment, and then passed on by inheritance.

GEORGES LOUIS LECLERC DE BUFFON

Buffon was a French natural philosopher (1707-1788) who tried to fit the known phenomena of nature into a rigid system governed by physical laws. He emphasized the importance of scientific experimentation as well as that of observation.

arose, for Lamarck's theory attracted little attention. Not for two generations would Charles Darwin demonstrate the reverse truth—that only giraffes with long necks survive to produce more of their kind. And not for a century would geneticists learn that the only characteristics that can be inherited are those "acquired" in the slow, evolutionary way—at conception, and not after birth.

At college Darwin also encountered the Greek view of creation. Thales, in the Sixth Century B.C., had studied the abounding life of the Aegean Sea and declared water to be "the mother from which all things arose and out of which they exist." Heraclitus had written that everything is "transposed into new shapes." And Aristotle had maintained in the clearest of arguments that there was a natural procedure from plants to plant-animals to animals and then, by graduated steps, to man.

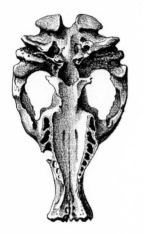

The Toxodon, whose fossilized head was discovered by Darwin on the Argentine pampas, contributed to the theory of evolution. It fortified Darwin's belief that related species were not created separately, but evolved from common ancestors.

BUT none of this—the philosophical insights of the Greeks, the premonitions of Erasmus Darwin or the well-worked-out theory of Lamarck—had prevailed as the 1830s began. For the Bible declared: "And God said: Let the waters bring forth abundantly the moving creature that hath life. . . . Let the earth bring forth the living creature after his kind. . . . Let us make man in our image. . . ." Time and western society had further narrowed the majestic words of Genesis to mean the sudden, independent, miraculous creation of all life in the year 4004 B.C. The year was fixed in the mid-17th Century by Archbishop James Ussher, later appeared in the margins of many Bibles and was widely accepted as the true time of creation. Only Noah's Flood, it was argued by many distinguished scholars, lay and divine, had rearranged the original order and reshaped life and landscape into the forms known to the 19th Century.

All of this was more than a belief; it was a tenet of faith, the foundation on which society stood, the base of man's special status in the universe. Even as Charles Darwin read the contrary, evolutionary views of his grandfather and others, he had no intention of challenging so primal a principle. He was not a particularly rebellious young man.

An invitation to join the *Beagle* on her second extensive exploratory-scientific expedition came soon after Darwin had taken his degree at Cambridge. Charles was all excited eagerness to go. And the Reverend Henslow had written that there "never was a finer chance for a man of zeal and spirit." Dr. Darwin was just as strongly opposed; he did not want another change of profession. Only after the Wedgwoods had urgently intervened in Charles's behalf did the doctor yield and agree to finance the trip for his son. "*Gloria in excelsis,*" Charles exulted in writing the good news to Henslow.

Darwin drew this conclusion because the Toxodon bore close resemblance to the elephant (there were many anatomical similarities) and the rhinoceros (it had the same thick, columnar legs). But he erred in thinking they were related.

On the 27th of December, 1831, the *Beagle* sailed from Devonport. The 235-ton brig scarcely had sailed beyond sight of land when Darwin became seasick. As he lay in his hammock he read a new book Henslow had recommended, Volume I of Charles Lyell's *Principles of Geology*.

"Read it by all means," wrote Henslow, "for it is very interesting, but do not pay any attention to it except in regard to facts, for it is altogether wild as far as theory goes." Lyell was arguing that the earth's continents, plains and mountains were shaped not by Noah's Flood, but by the action of the rains, the winds, earthquakes, volcanoes and other natural forces. The forces were exactly the same, said Lyell, as those still altering the earth: "No causes whatever have from the earliest time to which we can look back, to the present, ever acted but those now acting and they have never acted with different degrees of energy from which they now exert."

To the scientist Henslow such ideas were wild. To the Reverend Adam Sedgwick, Darwin's professor of geology at Cambridge, the book's denial that the earth was molded by the Flood was heretical, shocking and irreligious. But to Darwin, reading Lyell as the *Beagle* sailed southward and as he watched the moon and stars "performing their small revolutions in their new apparent orbits," a new and dazzling array of ideas soon appeared.

On January 16 the *Beagle* came to anchor at Praia in the Cape Verde Islands. It was Darwin's first and fervently anticipated sight of the tropics. Tamarinds, bananas and palm trees—the whole brilliantly colored scene was "overwhelming and glorious." When he could bring his thoughts down to what he called "geologising," he noticed a broad band of white stretching for miles along the face of the sea cliff. Climbing up to investigate, he found embedded in the white calcareous stone thousands of sea shells, many of them like the shells he had gathered on the beach below.

With the guidance of Lyell's book, Darwin could make out an astounding story. The white shell bed once had been a part of the sea bottom. At some time in the past, a stream of lava had flowed into the sea and covered it. The heat had converted the top layer partly into a crystalline limestone and partly into a compact, spotted stone. Later still, some force had uplifted the entire coast until the onetime sea bottom stood 45 feet above the water. By thus observing and putting together many separate facts, the hidden history of the past could be read and the present world understood.

As the *Beagle* sailed on toward Brazil through calm and sunny seas, Darwin had a long, bag-shaped seine towed behind her. He studied and compared the little fish and marine organisms that he hauled in, often in large numbers. Were some of them new or unknown species? If they differed from organisms already known to science, how did they differ?

Even more striking and upsetting to him were the relationships between the animals of the past and those of the present. Along an old river bed on the Argentine pampas, Darwin noticed some fossil bones projecting from the gravel and red mud. He began to dig. Within an area of about 200 square yards he unearthed the remains of nine monstrous quadrupeds, all belonging to species long since extinct. One, the *Toxodon*, equaled an elephant in size and yet its teeth were those of a gnawer—an order that in modern times includes mostly the smaller quadrupeds. The position of its eyes, ears and nostrils suggested that it probably had been aquatic.

In another section of the pampas he dug up a decayed tooth of a horse. The fossil lay in the same stratum with teeth of the *Toxodon* and mastodon and the bony armor of a gigantic, armadillolike animal. Surprised to encounter the tooth of a horse, Darwin made sure that it had been embedded contemporaneously with the other remains. Its presence testified that the horse had been among the ancient inhabitants of the continent. And yet *Equus* had disappeared long before the first Spanish settlers arrived.

"Certainly it is a marvellous fact in the history of the Mammalia that in South America a native horse should have lived and disappeared, to be succeeded in after ages by the countless herds descended from the few introduced with the Spanish colonists," Darwin wrote.

The fossil species Darwin was uncovering on the pampas closely resembled the known fossil animals of North America. In more recent times each continent had housed its own distinctive animal population—South America its monkeys, llama, tapir, anteater and armadillo, and North America its own gnawers and its hollow-horned ruminants, the sheep, ox, goat and antelope.

"The more I reflect on this case, the more interesting it appears," Darwin noted. "I know of no other instance where we can almost mark the period and manner of the splitting up of one great region into two well-characterized zoological provinces." What caused the split, he figured, was the elevation of the Mexican platform and the submergence of land in the West Indies; thereafter only a few wanderers had managed to travel between the two continents.

Darwin also realized that the ancient animals of both continents were closer to the animals of Asia and Europe than were living American species. This probably meant, he decided, that the North American elephants, mastodons, horses and hollow-horned ruminants had migrated from Siberia over a land bridge in the area of the Bering Strait. They gradually made their way to the southern continent, where they flourished but finally became extinct.

What had extinguished the giant quadrupeds whose fossilized bones were scattered across the pampas? Darwin never found out—and neither has anyone else—but he concluded that "certainly no fact in the long history of the world is so startling as the wide and repeated exterminations of its inhabitants."

The Fuegian Indians inhabited the southern tip of South America and struck Darwin as an extremely sturdy people. They swam in icy waters without ill effect, wore only skimpy guanaco-skin capes like the one above and used primitive Stone Age tools. Once several thousand strong, the four tribes of the Fuegians have today been reduced to a few scattered individuals by disease, liquor and forced relocation.

TIME was taking on new dimensions and life new relationships by December 1832 when the *Beagle* sailed into the stormy waters off Tierra del Fuego at the tip of the continent. As the brig dropped anchor in the Bay of Good Success, a band of Fuegian natives, uttering wild cries, greeted her from the edge of the dense and gloomy forest that extended down to the shore. The next morning Darwin accompanied the *Beagle* party which went ashore to negotiate with them. Broad transverse bands of red and white streaked the face of the leader. Their only clothing consisted of guanaco skins thrown across the shoulders, "leaving their persons as often exposed as covered," Darwin noted. One woman, nursing a newborn baby, later stood for hours watching the ship while sleet fell and melted on her naked bosom and the naked skin of the child.

Darwin was getting his first insight into the great differences between peoples. He marveled that a human tribe could survive so inhospitable and bleak an environment, but despite its rigors, the Fuegians did not seem to be dying out. Nature, Darwin concluded, had fitted man at Tierra del Fuego "to the climate and the productions of his miserable country."

More than another year was spent backtracking along the east coast of South America and on a return visit to Tierra del Fuego. It was June 1834, in the depth of winter, before the *Beagle* entered the Pacific to spend months working her way up the west coast. One day, on the island of Chiloé, as Darwin stretched out on the ground for a brief rest, he suddenly felt the earth rock beneath him. The movement reminded him of that of a vessel caught in a cross rip. The shock he felt was a tremor from the earthquake of February 20, 1835, one of many severe ones in the region's long record of disturbances.

For three years Darwin had been studying the elevation and subsidence of the land along the coasts of South America. Here the process occurred almost before his eyes. A few days after the earthquake, he made measurements at Concepción Bay which showed that the land had risen between two and three feet. Thirty miles away Captain Robert Fitzroy discovered putrefying mussels still clinging to rocks 10 feet above the high-water mark.

The mighty climax to the region's vast earth-stirrings lay just ahead—the Andes. In a crossing of the mountains, Darwin came upon sea shells embedded in the rocks at 13,000 feet. He could identify many of them—*Gryphaea, Ostrea, Turratella*—and he noted that he "reaped a grand harvest."

At night, listening to the Andes torrents, he could comprehend the other phase of the earth's slow shaping—the wearing-down of mountains. What could withstand these rushing waters? Darwin thought too of the vast plains of sand and shingle that he had seen on the eastern side of the continent. He had wondered how such a mass could have accumulated. Now he understood.

IN September 1835 the *Beagle* headed westward into the Pacific to the Galápagos Islands. The dry, volcanic archipelago at first looked desolate. The only plants struck Darwin as "wretched-looking weeds," and the brushwood seemed as bare as an English oak in winter. As he walked across Chatham Island's rugged lava surface, he suddenly met two huge tortoises—about 200 pounds each—ambling along a well-beaten path. In the strange, Cyclopean setting they resembled something antediluvian, Darwin thought. He later learned that the Galápagos were the tortoises' original home; no other species like them had developed anywhere else in the world.

To Darwin's growing amazement, this phenomenon was repeated. Great black lizards, some four feet long, sunned themselves on the black rocks along the shore. Darwin had read that they often went to sea "in herds a-fishing." The careful naturalist opened the stomachs of several specimens and found them distended with minced seaweed. Not only was the black lizard herbivorous, it was that extraordinary creature, a seagoing lizard.

A rust-colored, terrestrial lizard, whose burrows so filled the earth on James Island that it was difficult for the *Beagle* party to find a place to pitch a tent, also was aboriginal. And together the two species of lizard constituted a genus, or group of related species, to be found only in these islands.

Darwin pressed on with his collections, seeking as usual to obtain at least one specimen of each species. All 15 kinds of sea fish he caught were new species and 15 of the 16 land shells he collected. And so were nearly all of the insects and many of the flowering plants.

The birds of the archipelago were even more remarkable. Darwin shot or captured 26 kinds, and all except one far-ranging, larklike finch were peculiar to the islands. Among them were 13 finches—"a most singular group of finches," for all resembled one another in the structure of their beaks, in the form of their bodies and in their plumage, and yet each constituted a species.

"Seeing this gradation and diversity of structure in one small, intimately related group of birds, one might really fancy that from an original paucity of birds in this archipelago, one species had been taken and modified for different ends," Darwin wrote, coming close to and yet still shying away from admitting that species were not immutable but had evolved from one ancestor. Only as he entered the details about the birds in his special little ornithology notebook did he put his doubts into words. Such facts, he jotted down, might well "undermine the stability of species."

If the aboriginal Galapageian species had differed radically from those in the rest of the world, Darwin's gathering doubts about special creation might have been stilled. Most of them, however, bore a marked resemblance to related groups on the American mainland, some 500 to 600 miles over the sea.

"It was most striking," he wrote, "to be surrounded by new birds, new reptiles, new shells, new insects, new plants, and yet by innumerable trifling details of structure and even by the tones of voice and plumage of the birds to have the temperate plains of Patagonia, or rather the hot dry deserts of Northern Chile, vividly brought before my eyes.'' If new and different beings had been placed on the islands at the time of creation, why did they bear the American stamp? Such questions ran persistently through Darwin's puzzled and shaken thoughts as the *Beagle* prepared to leave the strange subworld of the Galápagos.

A few days before the sailing, the vice governor of the islands happened to remark that he could always tell from which island any one of the Galápagos' great tortoises came. For a time the remark almost slipped by Darwin.

"I never dreamed that islands 50 and 60 miles apart, and most of them in sight of each other, formed of precisely the same rocks, placed under a quite similar climate, rising to a nearly equal height, would have been differently tenanted," he explained.

Darwin learned that the shells of the tortoises from Charles Island turned up in front, like Spanish saddles, while those from James Island were rounder and blacker. What was more, all the mocking thrushes from Charles belonged to one species; all from Albemarle to another. The insects and plants also differed from island to island.

"It is the circumstance that several of the islands possess their own species of the tortoise, mocking-thrush, finches, and numerous plants, these species having the same general habits, occupying analogous situations, and obviously filling the same place in the natural economy of this archipelago, that strikes me with wonder," said Darwin. Characteristically he did not stop with wonder, but sought an explanation. Although the islands lay close together, the strong ocean currents running between them blocked all natural water-borne inter-island transport. The islands also were remarkably free of winds that might blow birds, seeds or insects from one to another. Furthermore, the profound depth of the ocean around the islands and their volcanic nature made it unlikely that they ever had been united. Each in a sense stood as a separate world.

Darwin still could not quite concede that brand-new species had evolved from the very few migrants that had made their way to the Galápagos and from island to island, but skepticism of the old belief showed through his comment: "One is astonished at the amount of creative force, if such an expression may be used, displayed on these small, barren, and rocky islands; and still more so, at its diverse yet analogous action on points so near each other."

O N October 2, 1836, the *Beagle* made the shores of England. Most of Darwin's vast collections had been shipped home long since. So had most of his little notebooks and his meticulously kept journal; in them he had recorded the ineffable variety of the earth and its relationships—continent to continent, continent to island, species to species and past to present.

His observations and findings would upset many cherished theories about the coral atolls, the rise of the Andes and the past life of the earth. But it was another long conclusion that Darwin was drawing from all that he had seen as he circumnavigated the globe that would lastingly alter the world's thought. Now 27 and a well-seasoned naturalist, he was already seeking a better explanation than special creation to account for the observable, undeniable basic unity of the entire living world. Would not all the myriad likenesses and differences become understandable if all life had evolved from the same ancestry? His answer was reserved for the future. When Darwin hurried off the *Beagle* into the rainy dusk at Falmouth, he was an impatient young man with but one thought—to get back home.

UNCONCERNED BY DOZENS OF SCUTTLING CRABS, A SEA-LION HERD BASKS BY ITS PRIVATE POOL ON A SURF-BATTERED GALAPAGOS SHORE

A Showcase for Evolution

On his voyage around the world, Darwin found that isolation had thrust some unlikely creatures into startling roles. In the Galápagos Islands great tortoises were grazing like cattle, and the finch population had diversified until it filled many niches normally occupied by other birds. And in Tierra del Fuego he found human beings who were wonderfully adapted to a bitterly cruel climate.

THE GRASSY HIGHLANDS get plenty of rainfall on Indefatigable Island, where ferns and mosses flourish by fresh-water pools. The whole Galápagos archipelago is pocked with thousands of volcanic craters, some rising more than 4,000 feet above the sea.

The Strange Subworld of the Galápagos

The Galápagos Islands thrust their bleak profiles from the Pacific Ocean some 600 miles west of Ecuador, astride the equator. The archipelago (*below*) comprises 14 islands—of which the largest is 75 miles long—plus innumerable rocks and islets. The product of cataclysmic underwater eruptions, the islands present a forbidding aspect of barren coasts and infernal fields of lava rock strewn with cactus. On the mountains, however, where the trade winds drop their moisture, the vegetation is lush (*above*). But it is the fauna of the islands that make them so unusual. Reptiles and birds have thrived here; insects are comparatively scarce; and there are only two native mammals, a small rat and a bat. Descending from a few stranded ancestors and cut off from the rest of the world, the Galápagos animals offer much more obvious proofs of the fact of evolution than can be seen in the more intricate complexes of life in most environments. When he came here, Darwin was just beginning to puzzle about the origin of species. What he saw in the Galápagos gave him insights without which his historic theory might not have been constructed.

ABOARD THE "BEAGLE," DARWIN SPENT FIVE WEEKS EXPLORING THE GALAPAGOS ISLANDS

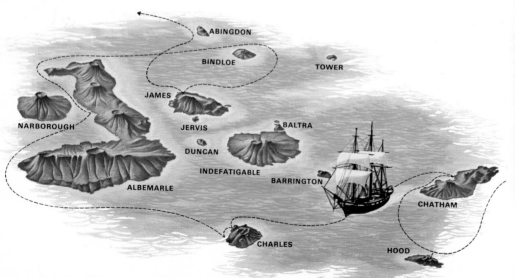

ABINGDON

BINDLOE

TOWER

JAMES

NARBOROUGH

JERVIS

DUNCAN

BALTRA

INDEFATIGABLE

BARRINGTON

ALBEMARLE

CHATHAM

CHARLES

HOOD

THE DESERT-DRY LOWLANDS of Barrington Island are all but sterile, studded with hardy prickly-pear cactus trees, some growing 30 feet tall. Though hot, the islands' climate is more temperate than that in most equatorial regions because of the cool Humboldt Current that sweeps up the west coast of South America from the Antarctic and veers northwest to the Galápagos.

A COLORFUL IGUANA dwelling only on Hood Island is brighter-hued and smaller than other sea iguanas. All have strong claws for clinging to the rocks, and blunt snouts for eating seaweed.

The World's Only Seagoing Lizards

The oddest inhabitants of the Galápagos coastlines are the marine iguanas, which exist nowhere else in the world. Like miniature dinosaurs, the inky, armored lizards swarm over the rocky shores of the islands. When upset they squirt vapor from their nostrils like storybook dragons. Despite their ferocious appearance the sea iguanas are strict and docile vegetarians, completely harmless and gregarious to an extreme *(left)*. Though armed with strong claws and sharp teeth, they rarely use them on each other and never attack other animals. These aquatic reptiles are skillful swimmers that subsist entirely on the abundant seaweed which grows underwater on rocks. But the iguanas do not ordinarily venture beyond the safety of the feeding grounds at their doorsteps, probably because of the swift ocean currents running between the islands and the roaming sharks that infest the deeper waters. Thus there has been little opportunity for insular interbreeding, and they have developed several different races that are generally similar but vary slightly from one island to another.

DRAB MARINE IGUANAS blend into the rocks of Narborough Island. They sun all day except when feeding on seaweed at low tide. They grow about three feet long and average 20 pounds.

21

A QUIET BROWSE in a tree absorbs a land iguana. This species also relishes juicy cactus pads, chewing the flesh and swallowing the sharp spines whole. Cactus fills most of its water needs.

The Odd Landlubber Lizards

Inland lives another grotesque lizard, the land iguana, which never mingles with the seagoing variety. Darwin noted that "these two species agree in their general structure and in many of their habits"; but they differ as the result of evolutionary changes so that each has adapted to its environment. The land iguana lives on leaves and cactus plants and climbs trees (above), while the marine iguana swims to get to its seaweed. The marine iguana has partially webbed toes and a flattened tail for more effective swimming; the land species has normal toes and a stout round tail.

No one is sure how iguanas got to the Galápagos archipelago in the first place. The most likely theory is based on the marvelous ability of reptiles to go for long periods without food or water. A few South American lizards could have survived on natural rafts that drifted in the ocean currents and finally reached the islands. Such occasional voyages, made unknown millions of years ago, could account for the whole teeming populations of distinct reptilian species now inhabiting the world of the Galápagos.

A BLOODY DUEL occurs between two male iguanas in a territorial dispute as they lock jaws (top), then draw apart. Such fights are rare; most quarrels between iguanas are bluffing matches.

A SUNNY SIESTA is a favorite activity of all iguanas, which are lazy and quite tame. At night land iguanas sleep in shallow burrows that they dig; the sea kind retire to cracks in the rocks.

The Imperiled Patriarch of the Archipelago

Although the struggle for existence is waged under the same rules everywhere on earth, life in the Galápagos takes on the appearance of a mad fantasy because of the islands' remarkable cast of characters. Except for a few rice rats, no land mammals survived the rigorous driftwood journey from the mainland of South America. They simply never arrived to fill their customary niches; in their absence the hardier reptiles developed into unique species playing unique roles.

The colossus of the archipelago is the giant tortoise that gave its Spanish name—*galápago*—to the islands. These great reptiles weigh as much as a quarter of a ton, with shells as big as bathtubs. Before the clumsy hand of man interfered, tortoises had a life expectancy of well over a century. But man discovered that they were an ideal source of fresh meat on long voyages, since they could survive for weeks tied down on the decks of ships. Two centuries of indiscriminate slaughter pushed them to the brink of extinction. Not until 1959 was a sanctuary created to protect all the islands' wildlife.

Man was also responsible for introducing other mortal enemies to the tortoise. Pirates and whalers brought goats, sheep and donkeys to the islands as future sources of food. Not only did these eat the vegetation that the tortoises needed for sustenance but they also destroyed the natural cover that protected young tortoises from attack by marauding gulls and hawks. In 1964 a group of conservationists finally succeeded in establishing a program to rid the islands of goats. There may yet be hope for the grand patriarch of the Galápagos.

CHARACTERISTIC CARAPACES distinguish tortoises of different islands. The round, black shell is from James Island, the other comes from Hood Island. Ten of the principal islands have had one or more varieties, several of which are already extinct.

A MONSTER ON THE MOVE can travel around 360 yards an hour, a speed Darwin clocked. Baby tortoises, not yet invulnerable like this one, are defenseless against the wild dogs and pigs first imported by settlers. Today few young tortoises survive.

SHOWING OFF, a male frigate bird displays its bright gular pouch to attract female attention during courtship and nest-building. The pouch stays inflated in flight and even when the bird is asleep. The hooked bill can be dipped in the water during full flight to snatch food. This aggressive marauder, distantly related to the pelican, is also known as the man-of-war bird.

An Inflatable, Piratical Bird

Besides reptiles, the Galápagos archipelago supports a huge population of birds. Having originally flown there or been blown there by storms, some of the birds have since developed into interesting species found nowhere else. The flamboyant frigate bird—sporting its remarkable red pouch during courtship (*opposite*)—has not changed radically from its cousins in other tropical climates, but the population of the Galápagos variety constitutes a separate race. Though a stay-at-home, the frigate bird is a superb flier, as well as an unmitigated pirate. In feeding, it hovers gracefully above other birds, waits for one to catch a fish, then swoops unerringly to the attack, forcing the victim to drop its prize. The frigate bird then snatches the falling fish in mid-air, gulps it down and climbs aloft to wait for another morsel.

WELCOMING ITS MATE, an egg-sitting male bestows a caress. After nest-building, its pouch deflates. The female lays one egg each year, and must protect the chick from other frigate birds.

BUILDING NESTS, a colony of frigate birds roosts in the tops of low bushes. They rob unguarded nests of other birds to find building materials. Weighing only three and a half pounds with a four-ounce skeleton, they have over-seven-foot wingspreads and are capable of long, soaring flight. However, they cannot take off from water and seldom fly far from the sight of land.

27

THE BLUE-FOOTED BOOBY raises its young on the bare Galápagos rocks. At the equator, the main task of incubation is a matter of shading eggs from the baking heat of the sun's rays.

THE RED-FOOTED BOOBY is the only booby in the world that has learned to roost in trees, thus eliminating conflict for nesting space with its blue-footed relative. Both kinds live on fish.

A FLIGHTLESS CORMORANT GUARDS ITS YOUNG. ONE OF THE EARTH'S RAREST BIRDS, THE SPECIES LIVES ONLY IN TWO GALAPAGOS ISLANDS

Birds That Know No Fear

The odd birds on these pages have all evolved into organisms distinctive in form and behavior from relatives anywhere else. Since the islands have few predators, many birds are not adapted to cope with them. Thus the flightless cormorant, which swims to catch its food and lives on the ground (*opposite, below*), has no need to fly; its wings have dwindled to vestigial stubs. In the relatively short time since man invaded the islands, most of the birds have not yet learned to fear him and are so tame they can be picked up in the hand. This naive acceptance of man as just one more large, peaceable animal is characteristic of nearly all the indigenous Galápagos fauna.

THE GALAPAGOS MOCKINGBIRD, much larger than its mainland relatives, usually rakes the ground for insect food, but on occasion enjoys a feast of blue-footed booby eggs (*above*).

THE SWALLOW-TAILED GULL BREEDS ONLY IN THE GALAPAGOS ISLANDS, BUT SOMETIMES MAKES VISITS TO SOUTH AMERICA'S WEST COAST

THE LARGE GROUND FINCH has developed a blunt, powerful beak for breaking open hard seeds, but also eats flowers, fruits and some insects. It can eat bigger seeds than other ground finches (*below*) and so it is not in direct competition with the smaller birds. Like all finches in the group, this one builds covered nests and lays eggs that are white with pink spots.

INSECT EATER

WARBLER FINCH

FAMILY shows types and beak shapes of Galápagos finches. Which type they descended from is not known. A similar species of finch lives in the Cocos Islands 400 miles to the north.

PLANT EATER

VEGETARIAN TREE FINCH

PRIMARILY INSECT EATERS PLUS SOME PLANTS

LARGE INSECTIVOROUS TREE FINCH

MEDIUM INSECTIVOROUS TREE FINCH

SMALL INSECTIVOROUS TREE FINCH

TOOL-USING FINCH

MANGROVE FINCH

PRIMARILY PLANT EATERS PLUS SOME INSECTS

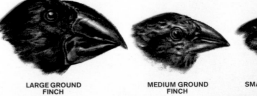

LARGE GROUND FINCH

MEDIUM GROUND FINCH

SMALL GROUND FINCH

SHARP-BEAKED GROUND FINCH

CACTUS GROUND FINCH

LARGE CACTUS GROUND FINCH

THE TOOL-USING FINCH is one of nature's rarest phenomena: a bird which uses an implement to get its food. Since there are no woodpeckers in the Galápagos, this finch has been able to fill the woodpecker's normal niche, but it lacks that bird's long tongue for extracting insects from the holes it chips in bark. So the finch has learned to use a cactus spine to do the job.

Darwin's "Most Singular Group of Finches"

When Darwin returned to England he had not yet challenged the belief that all animals were created as they are, and had never changed. It was only after analyzing his collection of Galápagos finches that he seriously began to question special creation. It was "a most singular group of finches": there were 13 species which showed differences in form and plumage but which were basically alike. Though the beaks were different, for example, they exhibited a perfect gradation in size (*opposite*). It was asking too much of coincidence, Darwin felt, to assume that all 13 species should have been separately created and still have so much in common. It was more logical to infer that it all started with one kind which in some way and for some reason had produced a family of widely varied relatives. An explanation for the phenomenon was suggested by the scarcity of other birds on the islands, which meant the finches had only each other to compete with. Then, in the struggle for available insects, a finch which, by an accident of heredity, became able to crack open and live on seeds, would have an advantage over those that had to rely solely on insects.

In time, and particularly if finches which had such slight differences were isolated on different islands so that the various populations could not interbreed, various species with different habits and different appearances would emerge. Thus, Darwin reasoned, evolution working over millions of years in these special conditions had fashioned numerous finch species, many of them filling roles which are held by other birds in other regions of the world.

Tierra del Fuego

Men Adapted to a Savage Land

When Darwin arrived in Tierra del Fuego aboard the *Beagle* in 1832, he was appalled by the primitive conditions in which the inhabitants of "this savage land" lived. He saw stark-naked Indians canoeing through rough seas in summer temperatures between 35° and 45° F. At night they slept naked on the wet, near-frozen ground. How did the Fuegians, with seeming disregard for the elements, survive? Darwin decided that "nature by making habit omnipotent, and its effects hereditary, has fitted the Fuegian to . . . his miserable country." Darwin's reasoning was pure Lamarckism, but his observations were accurate: it is now known that the Fuegians' metabolic rate is higher than the human norm.

Here were men adapted in special ways to a special environment, as the early photographs on these and the next four pages show. But though the Fuegian Indians had thrived in the face of natural hazards, they were no match for the white man; his diseases and ways have destroyed nearly all of them.

NAKED IN THE SNOW, an Ona Indian takes aim with bow and arrow. He has draped his cape over his knees and holds his quiver in his mouth. His mustache has been painted on.

THE "BEAGLE'S" ROUTE meanders through the realms of the Ona (shaded area) and Yahgan (outlined area), two of the largest tribes of Indians then in Tierra del Fuego. This is the New World's southernmost inhabited land, where storms harass all living things and snow falls in every month of the year. Darwin described the climate as "tempestuous."

A FAMILY AT HOME shows how humble the Ona Indians' way of life was. Their house is made of guanaco hides, draped over a wooden frame. On rare pleasant days, like the one on which this photograph was taken, the hides are pulled back. The twisted beech trees indicate the effect of relentless winds from Antarctica, some 650 miles away.

A FAMILY ON THE MOVE trudges along the shore barefoot to a new campsite. The men, women and children are wrapped in guanaco fur, the hide sides of which the Onas coated with red paint and grease or saliva for insulation. The men carry weapons; the women, their babies and meager household belongings. Ona society provided nothing else.

FOUR ONAS DRESS UP AS GHOSTS FOR A CEREMONY INITIATING YOUNG MEN INTO THE TRIBE, THEIR BODIES PAINTED, AND

WEARING HEADDRESSES OF BARK OR HIDE. THE ONE AT RIGHT, REPRESENTING A BABY, IS COVERED WITH TUFTS OF FEATHERS

PLAYING DEAD in the ritual in which all the ghosts above appear, the initiates in the snow will be carried into a ceremonial hut and there "brought back to life."

TESTING THEIR STRENGTH at a rare tribal conclave, two unclad Ona warriors wrestle. The Onas regarded wrestling matches as duels and often settled disputes this way.

A Baptism by Ice

In contrast to the Onas, who were essentially a land and forest people, another tribe, the Yahgans, endured an even bitterer existence among the southernmost islands off Tierra del Fuego. To find food they had to spend more than half their days in canoes, a life that stunted their legs and exposed them to constant drenching by freezing seas. When food was located, securing it often involved other hazards —deep dives for mussels, a climb up a steep cliff to

A YOUNG HUNTER, poised for the throw, puts his weight behind a spear. Yahgans hunted penguins with such bone-tipped weapons.

A FLIMSY HUT offers scant protection to a family (*right*), but keeps the fire going. The Yahgans built only temporary shelters.

A BARK CANOE, with smoke rising from it, seems to be on fire. Actually the smoke is from a hearth; the Yahgans carried fire with them.

throttle a sleeping bird and bite off its head. Yahgan clothing, when worn at all, consisted of stiff seal and sea-otter skins. In such a harsh land it was not surprising that a Yahgan mother, after giving birth, would dip her baby in the icy sea to toughen it. The Yahgans, who are thought to have migrated long ago from the north, spoke a complex tongue with 32,000 words. Within a few years, as its possessors become extinct, it will be a dead language.

THE OLDEST MEMBER of the vanishing Yahgan tribe is Julie, who was 90 when her picture was taken *(below)* in 1958. She was also photographed in 1907 or 1908 *(left)*, when the tribe numbered 170. Now there are but half a dozen survivors.

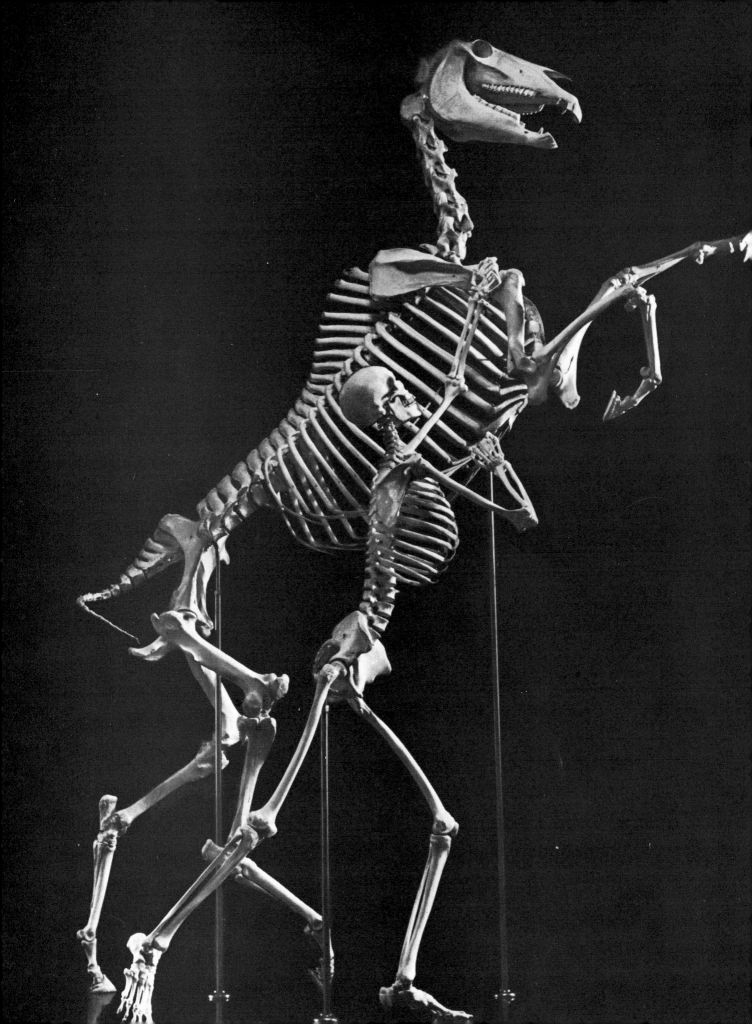

HORSE AND MAN exhibit in their skeletons similar bones in similar positions, but altered to perform different functions. In such relationships Darwin saw echoes of a primeval pattern, modified by evolution.

2

A Theory That Shook the World

MASSIVE fossil bones from the pampas crowded Charles Darwin's lodgings at Cambridge. He had returned to the university to edit his *Beagle* journal for publication and to catalog all the specimens he had collected on the voyage. As he thoughtfully examined the skull of an ancient fossil anteater, he noted the striking and complex ways in which this horse-sized monster of a distant past resembled small, living anteaters of today. The extinct animal bore every mark of being the ancestor of the modern, living animal. If it was, then every species on earth could *not* have been separately created by "elemental atoms" suddenly flashing into specialized living tissues. Many years later Darwin recalled in his autobiography that this was the moment when he fully faced this revolutionary, disturbing thought, the moment when he no longer could deny the undeniable.

Soon afterward, in March 1837, he went to London to finish work on his journal, which was to be known in the United States as *The Voyage of the Beagle*. As he arranged his Galápagos collections, he was impressed again by the likenesses some of the species showed. This time it was the resemblance of living species to living species that he could not pass over. Every structure, every line, every organ indicated that some of the island finches had developed in their own way from ancestors that had arrived from other islands of the archipelago. If each species had been independently created, why should some details have been repeated and others ignored?

Setting aside his doubts and scruples, Darwin wrote "Transmutation of Species" on the first page of a new notebook. In his diary he noted: "Had been greatly struck from about the month of previous March with character of South American fossils and species on Galapagos Archipelago. These facts (especially the latter) origin of all my views."

The idea of species haunted him, and yet to deal with the origin and relationships of all living and extinct groups would certainly be more work than he or any man could dare to contemplate. At the least it would require studies of comparative anatomy, instinct, heredity, metaphysics and the thousands of species proper. As he shrank before the task, Darwin thought of how Charles Lyell had begun by collecting all the facts he could find on geologic change. Perhaps if all the facts were collected that bore in any way on the variations in plants and animals in nature and under domestication, the whole imposing subject might be made sensible as Lyell had made sense out of geology.

THOMAS ROBERT MALTHUS

An English economist and a sociologist (1766-1834), Malthus believed that poverty and illness are unavoidable since population increases faster than the means of subsistence; that only famine, disease and war keep the world's population in check.

D ARWIN had his point of beginning. It was soon clear to him that the passkey to the breeder's results was selection: if a breeder wanted a swifter horse, he bred the fastest to the fastest. But how was selection carried on in nature, where there was no breeder to pick and choose, and no record book? Darwin puzzled at length over this problem. Then in October 1838 he happened to read Thomas Malthus' already famous "An Essay on the Principle of Population." Malthus argued that the human race would overrun the earth if not held in check by war, famine and disease. He pictured a constant, unrelenting struggle.

"It at once struck me," said Darwin, "that under these circumstances favourable variations would tend to be preserved and unfavourable ones to be destroyed." The struggle itself then performed the selecting function of the breeder. As the better-adapted survived and the ill-adjusted were eliminated each creature would tend to improve in relation to the conditions it lived in. In the long run such improvement would bring the formation of groups different enough from their predecessors to constitute new species—groups which in general interbreed with no others.

"I had at last got a theory by which to work," Darwin wrote. Cautious and modest as ever, he did not allow himself the satisfaction of making a brief abstract of this radical theory until 1842. It ran to 35 pages. Two years later he enlarged it to a 230-page essay and showed it to a few friends. In the sketch of 1842 and the essay of 1844 were all the major proposals that later, much later, were embodied in *The Origin of Species*.

SIR JOSEPH DALTON HOOKER

He was an English botanist (1817-1911) and the director of the famous Kew Botanical Gardens. A friend and supporter of Darwin, Hooker wrote extensively on the flora of New Zealand and Tasmania after a long scientific expedition to the area.

Darwin had married his cousin Emma Wedgwood, granddaughter of the potter Wedgwood, and soon after the 1842 sketch was written they fled the distractions of "vile, smoky" London. They bought a country house, Down, about 16 miles from town. His health had become precarious, but in the tranquil routine of the country he finished a new edition of the journal, a brilliant book on the formation of coral atolls and two books on the geologic discoveries of the voyage. All his materials from the long trip were now accounted for—except for one barnacle not much bigger than the head of a pin.

Darwin had come upon it on the coast of Chile, burrowing into a shell instead of clinging as all proper barnacles did. Before he pressed on with his work on species, he felt that it should be studied. He also questioned his right to discuss the problem of speciation without having worked out his due share of species. His scrupulousness carried him into eight long years of work on barnacles. Tedious and wearing though this study of classification was, it taught Darwin how the simplest of animals can vary in all their parts.

In 1854, with the last of 10,000-odd tiny barnacles shipped out of the house, Darwin wrote his friend Sir Joseph Dalton Hooker, director of the Kew Botanical Gardens, that he was resuming his work on species. Both Hooker and the geologist Lyell urged him to get on with it. Even so it was three years later before he even began the comprehensive book he had been planning for so long. By June 1858, eleven chapters were drafted. But Darwin might have buried himself in his vast subject for another decade or more if an incredible turn of events had not hustled him into putting it in print. In his mail on June 18 came an essay by Alfred Russel Wallace, a naturalist in Malaya with whom Darwin had been corresponding. It was titled "On the Tendency of Varieties to Depart Indefinitely from the Original Type." In a few pages Wallace had summarized the main points of the theory on which Darwin had spent over two decades.

Stunned, Darwin hurried off a note to Lyell: "I never saw a more striking coincidence. . . . So all my originality, whatever it may amount to, will be smashed, though my book, if it will ever have any value, will not be deteriorated, as all the labour consists in the application of the theory." He said he would of course offer to submit Wallace's work for publication, although Wallace had asked him only to forward it, if he thought it worthy, to Lyell. Darwin wondered, though, if he could honorably publish his own sketch now: "I would far rather burn my whole book than that he or any other man should think I had behaved in a paltry spirit."

Both Lyell and Hooker, also informed of the crisis, acted fast. They proposed a joint presentation before the Linnean Society of Wallace's paper and Darwin's 1844 essay. They urged the society that in the interest of science Darwin should not be permitted to withhold his own work in favor of Wallace's, as Darwin was inclined to do. So on July 1, 1858, portions of both papers were read before the society, named for the great Swedish naturalist, Carl Linnaeus.

The Linnean members listened in shocked silence. Hooker wrote Darwin the next day that the subject was "too novel and too ominous for the old school to enter the lists before armouring." Nevertheless, a scheduled paper by another author asserting the fixity of species was withdrawn. At the insistence of his friends, Darwin began to prepare an abstract of his 11 chapters and the 1844 essay for early publication. To distinguish it from the definitive, four-volume book he had expected to write (but which he could hardly expect many people to read), he called it *An Abstract of an Essay on the Origin of Species and Varieties through Natural Selection*. Darwin yielded to the demand of his publisher, John Murray, that he shorten the main title to *On the Origin of Species*.

IT was published November 24, 1859. The first edition's 1,250 copies sold out the first day, and the storm that has never wholly abated quickly broke. The indignant *Quarterly Review* charged that the book and its theory "contradict the revealed relation of the creation to the Creator." Another publication accused Darwin of using "absurd facts to prop up his utterly rotten fabric of guess and speculation." Darwin had decided not to add to the prejudices against his views by discussing the origin of man in *The Origin of Species*. And yet he did not want "to deceive any honourable man" by concealing his views. He settled

ALFRED RUSSEL WALLACE

Also an Englishman, naturalist Wallace (1823-1913) developed a theory of evolution similar to Darwin's. It was based on his studies of comparative biology in Brazil and the East Indies. He also systematized the study of animal geography.

THOMAS HENRY HUXLEY

An English biologist (1825-1895) and the century's leading defender of Darwinism, he was, in his own right, a great authority on vertebrate and invertebrate anatomy. Huxley also developed a new basis for classifying Pacific marine life.

the problem by adding one meaningful sentence to his concluding chapter: "Much light will be thrown on the origin of man and his history."

That single sentence—the understatement of the age—and the implications of the whole book proved more than enough to arouse the furor Darwin feared. The *Athenaeum* went straight for the crucial point—man. The magazine roundly damned Darwin, describing "the belief that man descends from the monkeys" as being "wrought into something like a creed by Mr. Darwin." Even Lyell was dubious about including man, and less restrained critics denounced Darwin for degrading man to something no better than the beasts.

At the meeting of the British Association for the Advancement of Science at Oxford in June 1860, the outrage still was growing. Three papers attacking Darwin were presented, and the word spread that Samuel Wilberforce, the bishop of Oxford, would take the platform to "smash Darwin," who was not present. When the bishop appeared, a crowd of 700 filled every inch of the meeting room. For half an hour the bishop savagely tore into Darwin and then, turning to Thomas H. Huxley, a defender of Darwin, he icily put his famous, sneering question: Was it through his grandfather or grandmother that Huxley claimed descent from an ape?

"The Lord hath delivered him into mine hands!" Huxley whispered to his neighbor on the platform. The self-admitted "wildcat" in him thoroughly aroused, the biologist strode forth to answer. Reaching his climax, he told the audience that he would feel no shame at having an ape for an ancestor—but that he would indeed be ashamed of a brilliant man who plunged into scientific questions of which he knew nothing. In other words, Huxley would prefer an ape to the bishop for an ancestor, and the crowd had no doubt of his meaning.

Pandemonium broke forth at this direct insult to the clergy. Men jumped to their feet shouting. In the uproar, a Lady Brewster fainted. Admiral Fitzroy, the former captain of the *Beagle*, waved a Bible aloft, shouting that it, rather than the viper he had harbored on his ship, was the true and unimpeachable authority. Hooker said that his blood boiled in anger at the attack on Darwin. "Looks of bitter hatred were directed to those who were on Darwin's side," *Macmillan's Magazine* reported. Whether gentle Charles Darwin liked it or not, and he did not, the issue was fully joined—science versus religion.

"THE ORIGIN OF SPECIES" was one long argument based on three great facts and two deductions drawn from them. The first fact is that all living things vary. The second is that all living groups tend to increase in geometric ratio. The third is that the numbers of a species tend nevertheless to remain fairly constant. From these facts Darwin drew his two crucial deductions: there is a struggle for existence, and in that struggle the fittest survive.

Few could dispute that all living things vary. Each must know that he is different from all others—unless he is an identical twin. Why each individual should be born different, Darwin could not say. The laws of heredity would not become known for another 40 years, and Darwin readily confessed his ignorance of them. At other times, though, he persuaded himself that the use or disuse of a structure or organ might produce inheritable modifications and thus shape heredity. In this he veered very close to Lamarck and straight into grave error.

Darwin was acutely aware, however, that the birth of billions of varying individuals had not produced an inextricable chaos. On the contrary, the living universe was divided into groups subordinate to groups, and all the innumerable individuals were fitted to one another and to conditions of their lives. "We see

PIGEON EVOLUTION WROUGHT BY MAN

The common rock dove is thought to be the parent stock of some 300 domesticated breeds of fancy pigeons. Darwin, who was interested in the effects controlled breeding had on inheritance in plants and animals, classified the pigeons of his day.

The fantail is one of the most popular breeds of pigeons among both American and European fanciers. Originally white, it has been bred in many colors, including black, red and yellow. The first fantail birds may have been bred in Asia.

these beautiful co-adaptations most plainly in the woodpecker and the mistletoe," said Darwin, "and only a little less plainly in the humblest parasite which clings to the hairs of a quadruped or feathers of a bird; in the structure of the beetle which dives through the water; in the plumed seed which is wafted by the gentlest breeze; in short, we see beautiful adaptations everywhere and in every part of the organic world."

The second fact was as clearly discernible. Darwin could find no exception to the rule that every organic being naturally increases at so fast a rate that the progeny of a single pair, if not destroyed, would soon cover the earth. In Darwin's own day even slow-breeding man had doubled in numbers; he calculated that if humanity should increase at such a rate for 1,000 years, not even standing room would remain on the planet. Yet no one species had overrun the world. From these unquestionable facts, backed by a host of unassailable observations, Darwin came to his deduction: "A struggle for existence inevitably follows from the high rate at which all organic beings tend to increase."

The pouter was probably brought to Europe some five centuries ago by Dutch traders returning from India. Also bred in many colors, the pouter is notable for its immense, barrel-shaped chest and, in most species, for its long, slender legs.

B Y a struggle for existence Darwin did not mean simply a battle of tooth and claw. He included the dependence of one being on another, and not only merely the preservation of the life of the individual, but also success in leaving progeny. In this broad sense, a plant on the edge of the desert could be said to be engaged in a struggle against drought, or the mistletoe in a contest with other fruit-bearing plants to tempt the birds to devour it and disseminate its seeds.

A few homely experiments provided Darwin with statistical evidence on the struggle for life. On the well-mowed lawn outside his living-room window, he marked out a three-by-four-foot plot and let the grass grow. He knew that in such a natural free-for-all the more vigorous plants would kill off the others. In his little experimental plot, nine out of 20 species perished.

On a heath where cattle had browsed from time immemorial, one section was enclosed in Darwin's day and the cattle excluded. Soon a multitude of Scotch firs sprang up in the enclosure. While visiting relatives in the vicinity, Darwin went to the heath to investigate this natural change. For miles not a tree was to be seen on the open heath, though many firs grew on the ridges above it. But Darwin bent down to examine the close-cropped turf. In one square yard he counted 32 little trees, one of them displaying 26 rings of annual growth. The browsing of the cattle had stopped them from ever raising their heads above the stems of the heath. No wonder the trees sprang up by the millions when they suddenly were protected from the cattle.

In so inexorable a struggle, Darwin asked, "can we doubt (remembering that many more individuals are born than can possibly survive) that individuals having any advantage, however slight, over others, would have the best chance of surviving and procreating their kind?" It was his second all-important deduction, the one he chose to call "natural selection." He also accepted as accurate and convenient a term proposed by Herbert Spencer, "survival of the fittest."

If all members of any one group were born alike, survival would be a matter of chance. But Darwin emphasized that all are not alike. Some are stronger, some swifter, some better-clothed, some more, or less, conspicuous. The white of some ptarmigan more exactly matches the snow; the green of some leaf eaters that of the leaf. These are the most likely to survive. By the continued preservation of the individuals with the most favorable variations, Darwin pointed out, all living things become amazingly well-adapted to their environment and to the intricate web of life in which they exist.

The jacobin receives its name from its monklike hood of feathers. The controlled evolution of these feather conformations, particularly prized by breeders, has led to some bizarre strains in which the bird's feathers completely obliterate side vision.

But could the accumulation of minute variations be built into the wider differences characterizing species? The question went to the heart of Darwin's case. Common knowledge and his own careful data showed that by accumulating slight variations, men had been able to produce horses as different as the sleek Arabian and the stanch Percheron. The two breeds had become so different it was difficult to realize that both had sprung from a common ancestor. But what could produce such divergence in nature?

One day as Darwin was out riding in his carriage, the answer came to him. It was simple: "The more diversified the descendants of a species became in structure, constitution and habits, the better they would be able to seize on widely diversified places in nature." Mammals equipped to fly or swim or climb found new openings and new opportunities. The different survived and multiplied; less improved groups were extinguished.

Yet if life had sprung from one beginning and had occupied the earth by becoming different and moving into other dwellings, proof had to be supplied that it could have reached some of the most inaccessible parts of the world, such as the distant, oceanic islands. The peculiar life of such islands held no problem for those who believed in special creation, for creation could explain its presence by fiat. But if a single place on the earth was tenanted by life which could not have got there naturally, the whole case for evolution faced collapse.

No subject gives me so much doubt and difficulty as the means of dispersal of terrestrial productions on the oceanic islands," Darwin wrote to his cousin, William Darwin Fox. Darwin thought that seeds might have floated to the islands. Hooker, the expert botanist, contended that seeds would never grow after long immersion in salt water. Darwin's only recourse was to test. He placed seeds in bottles of salt water and dropped them in a tank of water cooled to 32°. After a week the seeds had emitted so much mucus that Darwin jokingly said he half expected them to turn into tadpoles. But when he planted them, they grew. In later experiments some seeds survived 137 days of immersion. In a sea current moving a mile an hour, seeds could be carried 168 miles in a week.

Perhaps there were other means of transport too. Darwin fed aquatic grass seed to fish at London's Zoological Gardens and then proffered the fish to storks. In due time the seeds were voided, and grew. Seeds also might float to distant islands on driftwood or be carried on the mud-caked feet of birds. It was harder to see how fresh-water shells could have bridged fatal stretches of salt water to reach fresh water on the islands. Darwin complained that the problem was driving him wild. He could see no solution until one day he noticed that ducks coming out of a pond had duckweed caught on their feet. Darwin glimpsed his answer; he knew that shells live on the weeds. He dangled the feet of a duck in an aquarium where fresh-water shells were just hatching. Immediately a number of them climbed aboard. They survived out of water for from 12 to 20 hours, time enough for a duck to fly 600 or 700 miles and alight on a fresh-water lake on some far island. Darwin also had explained the shells' mode of travel.

He could discover no way for the soft, slimy spawn of frogs to survive a long sea haul, or for mammals to make their way to islands never joined to the land. And significantly there were no frogs or land mammals on most isolated islands. Only those species able to survive the salt and the pounding of the sea, or to find a way to avoid it, had reached the islands. One by one, perhaps, they had floated or emplaned in. The life of the oceanic islands was no longer a difficulty of the theory of evolution; it was rather a strong proof of it.

In 1837, when Darwin was beginning his first notebook on species, he admitted that he "could not avoid" the thought that man came under the same laws as all other living things. But his attempt in *The Origin* to minimize the acute issue had failed. The whole discussion was loudly out in the open. Darwin hoped that Wallace or Lyell would write a book scientifically examining the problem of man's ancestry and position, but neither did. In time the scientific acceptance of his doctrines heartened Darwin to the point where he was willing to deal with the subject himself. So in February 1867, Darwin undertook the book. It became *The Descent of Man, and Selection in Relation to Sex.*

If man is descended from "some pre-existing form," Darwin acknowledged that affirmative answers would have to be given to four questions: Does man vary like the other animals? Does he increase so rapidly that there is a struggle for existence in which the most beneficial variations are preserved and the least favorable eliminated? Does his bodily form show traces, more or less plain, of his descent? Could his high, special qualities of mind and morality have been produced by evolution?

In *The Origin* he had already answered, with overwhelming evidence and for all species, the first two questions. Now he plunged into a four-year marshaling of fact and deduction bearing on the other two. In his view it was "notorious that man is constructed on the same general type or model as other mammals." This went for all the bones in his body, the structure of his brain, his reproductive processes, even his susceptibility to infection and parasites. Even stranger, man bore within him a number of vestigial organs, useless to his modern mode of life but useful in his past. There were the wisdom teeth, and the vermiform appendix, and the os coccyx, that eloquent remnant of a tail.

To Darwin the evidence was incontestable, and "it is only our natural prejudice, and that arrogance which made our forefathers declare that they were descended from demi-gods, which leads us to demur. . . ." Then what about man's mental powers and moral sense? Darwin set out to show that while the gulf between man and the highest apes is immense, the difference is in degree. Animals clearly could feel pleasure and pain; in terror their muscles trembled and their hearts palpitated like man's. Such faculties as maternal love, self-sacrifice, jealousy and love of praise, and such complex attributes as imitation, attention, memory and rudimentary reason were not the exclusive property of man.

As best he could, Darwin buttressed his arguments with tests. Curious about the curiosity of monkeys, he carried a stuffed snake into the monkey cage at the Zoological Gardens. After the first wild excitement quieted, the monkeys gathered around, ludicrously staring at it. Then Darwin brought in a paper bag containing a small live snake. One by one, the monkeys sidled up to peer into the bag for a peek at the dreadful object. To the argument that language is an impassable barrier between beasts and men, he offered the proof of his own pets that dogs can comprehend words and sentences, and pointed out that many birds, besides parrots, have the power of articulation.

The vast gap between the social instincts of an animal and the most elevated qualities of human beings seemed scarcely greater to Darwin than the distance between the mind of an idiot and that of a Newton, or between the most crude human society and the most civilized one. That there had been a progression from primitive to civilized man was not at all taken for granted in Darwin's time. Even while he was writing *The Descent of Man*, the Duke of Argyll, a respected scientist, published his *Primeval Man*, a book attempting to prove

The diving beetle (Dytiscus) struck Darwin as a fine example of how species adapt to their environments. Most beetles have long been land dwellers, but this one lives in the water, and has developed extra-long hind legs covered with brushlike hairs that serve both as oars and hearing organs. Nevertheless it can still exist on land for long periods, and is an excellent flier.

that man came into the world a civilized being. Savages, to the duke and to a wide segment of society, were simply men who had undergone degradation.

To Darwin, his own was a truer and more cheerful view—that man had risen, though by slow and interrupted steps, from "some primordial cell" through the fish, the amphibians and the mammals to an Old World simian stem. From that point on, he held, the development of upright posture and a larger brain could bring enough modification to produce modern man. But he constantly had to face the taunt: "Where are the missing links? Why has none of them been found?" In *The Descent* he could only say that the discovery of fossils is a slow and fortuitous process at best, and that the regions most likely to afford remains connecting man with his extinct ancestors had not been searched. He admitted with sorrow that the long pedigree he was giving man was not of "noble quality." But he saw no reason to be ashamed of it: "The most humble organism is something much higher than the inorganic dust under our feet; and no one with an unbiased mind can study any living creature, however humble, without being struck with enthusiasm at its marvellous structure and properties."

As he worked on his monumentally supported argument for the descent of life and man, he was troubled by a major difficulty. All animals of a species were subjected to the same conditions and the same struggle, and yet there were sexual differences, such as the greater size, strength and pugnacity of the male, its weapons of offense or means of defense, its gaudy coloring and ornaments, its power of song. Natural selection could not have produced such changes in one sex and not in the other, for natural selection depends upon the success of both sexes in relation to the conditions of life.

Darwin decided that there must be a second kind of selection, a sexual selection, dependent upon the success of certain individuals over others of the same sex in the propagation of offspring. "It seems to me almost certain that if the individuals of one sex were during a long series of generations to prefer pairing with certain individuals of the other sex . . . the offspring would slowly but surely become modified in the same manner," he wrote. In 13 lengthy chapters Darwin examined the results of sexual selection in all the large classes of the animal kingdom—the mammals, birds, fish, reptiles and crustaceans. It was, as Alfred Wallace said in a review, really a second book.

ON February 24, 1871, *The Descent of Man* was published. "On every side it is raising a storm of mingled wrath, wonder, and admiration," said the *Edinburgh Review*. The *Times* made up for a favorable review of *The Origin of Species* by printing a six-column article of pained disapproval. The writer held it deplorable that Darwin should cast doubt on man's God-given status at the very moment when the Commune had been established in Paris and dangerous, unsettling ideas were spreading in England. A bill had been proposed for the chartering of labor unions. Married women were being permitted to retain control of their property, and some women were even demanding the vote. Oxford and Cambridge had been opened to all, regardless of religion. It was no moment, the reviewer scolded, for Darwin to rock the foundations of society and the state.

Charles Darwin had gone far in accounting for the hitherto inexplicable likenesses and differences of the living world. All life is one, he had shown, because all life has arisen from one unremembered beginning. After 18 and a half centuries of the Christian Era and innumerable preceding centuries, the world had achieved—or rather, had thrust upon it—a new understanding. A new prospect opened, full of progress and of tumult.

A GIRAFFE BROWSING AMONG TREETOPS MAKES USE OF SPECIAL EQUIPMENT—A LONG NECK—WITH WHICH NATURAL SELECTION PROVIDED IT

Secrets of Survival

Edging into new niches as climates change, finding new foods and foiling new foes, attracting more mates—these are some of the slowly won victories of natural selection. In winning them, the world's millions of living species have adopted strange habits, brilliant markings, exquisite colorings, marvelous disguises—what Darwin called life's "ever-branching and beautiful ramifications."

47

THE MULTICOLORED FACE of the male mandrill baboon, as well as its purplish-blue and red rump, exerts an irresistible attraction for the female. These characteristics began to be fixed in the species as brilliantly marked males won more of the females.

The Importance of Being Attractive

The attraction of one living thing for another is a mighty influence on evolution. Darwin found that "beauty is sometimes even more important than success in battle," and the male most likely to succeed in leaving progeny is the one most capable of capturing the female's attention. Thus by sexual selection—the preference for one mate over another—have come about such secondary sexual characteristics as the mandrill's face above and the tail of the peacock at right. But though man may see the peacock's tail as something beautiful, the peahen sees it only as a flag that stimulates her responses to the male.

THE IRIDESCENT TAIL of the male peacock is the emblem with which it attracts its harem of two to five females. According to Darwin, the preference of the females "for the most beautiful males, rendered the peacock the most splendid of living birds."

A WASP IN A POLLINATING POSITION ON AN ORCHID

A Case of Mistaken Identity

In competing for the attention of insect pollinators, plants have developed flowers with a variety of attracting devices—fragrance, food and eye-catching colors. The tiny *Ophrys* orchid of Europe, North Africa and the Middle East has gone a step further and assumed the appearance of an insect. The orchid emits a special perfume to lure a male wasp. Responding to this exciting scent and to the magnetism exerted by the orchid's form and color, the deluded male alights with ardor on its counterfeit mate. The tactile stimulation of tiny hairs on the flower induces the wasp to take a position like the one in the photograph above. In attempting to mate with the sweet-smelling blossom, it dislodges pollen-bearing rods, which stick to its head or abdomen. Flying off, the wasp carries them to another seductive blossom, as in the picture opposite, and causes fertilization.

Though almost solely responsible for the *Ophrys* orchid's pollination, the wasp apparently gains nothing in return for its services. But so dependent is the orchid upon the wasp for fertilization that it is still in the process of adapting itself to the insect's copulation instinct. This suggests that further natural selection will render it more and more wasp-like. The wasp's preference for blossoms its own size, for example, seems already to have prevented the *Ophrys* orchid from developing bigger blooms.

STARTLINGLY INSECTLIKE blossoms of three varieties of *Ophrys* orchid (*right*) have shiny patches at their centers. Such reflecting areas help attract pollinating male wasps.

COMPULSIVELY DRAWN by its perfume, a wasp (*opposite*) approaches an *Ophrys* orchid. The pollen rods on its head are from another flower and will fertilize this one.

TREE HOPPERS on the stems of a rosebush look like thorns and thus escape the eye of birds. But when approached, they make the mistake of jumping—thereby giving away their disguise.

Hide-and-Seek

Imitation is an art at which many insects excel. Some, like the birch moth, are camouflaged to look like their backgrounds when at rest or, like the tree hoppers at left, to masquerade as inanimate objects. Others, like the *Caligo* butterfly above, startle their enemies with deceptive markings or impersonate dangerous animals, like the bumblebee moth at right. Scientists suggest, to explain such carbon-copying, that it was the insects best able to deceive predators that survived the longest and could reproduce in greatest numbers, and thus passed their defensive techniques along to their descendants.

A CALIGO BUTTERFLY has spots under its wings like the eyes of an owl. This is not a case of imitation, but of the "startle effect." By suddenly showing its spots, it may surprise and frighten away a predator.

IN THE GUISE OF A BEE, the moth at the left shares a pink flower with a real bee. The bumblebee moth matches the bee's form and color and, while it lacks a stinger, most birds do not know this and avoid it.

53

The Stones That Are Living Plants

The succulents from South Africa shown on these pages are called "stone plants" or "living stones," for they not only grow in stonelike shapes, but also have taken on the coloring of stones. So successfully have they blended with their surroundings that they frequently elude even the keenest collector's eye. Such anonymity serves them well: in South Africa's dry, rock-strewn landscapes they would have been browsed into extinction by hungry, thirsty animals if they looked edible. Yet this does not prevent the tough-skinned stone plants from sprouting attention-getting flowers once a year—nosegays for pollinating insects.

These stonelike plants are stony only in appearance. They store rain water in their fleshy tissue, sealing it within their tough skins, and draw upon

this supply during drought. One variety, the window plant, can survive underground, with only flat, translucent "windows" aboveground to let in the needed light.

Both the appearance and water-conserving mechanisms of stone plants, suiting them to harsh desert conditions, dramatically illustrate how adaptations evolve to meet the demands of extreme environments.

TINY FLOWERS cloak a stonelike succulent. Though not a true stone plant, this one has thick, tough leaves. Prior to breaking out in fragrant bloom, it hoists them into a stubby column.

ROUND "WINDOWS" of one variety of stone plant admit light to the plants which are almost completely buried in gravel. These windows are often the same color as their desert surroundings.

SMALL SPOTS help disguise the smooth leaves of another stone plant. The yellow flower, which rises from a cleft between the leaves, is around an inch and a half across, and without a stem.

A ROCK GARDEN suddenly comes to life when the stone plants in it throw off their camouflage and burst into bloom (left). The variety growing here is called silverskin, after its silvery leaves.

ADDING A LEAF to its treasure-trove, the great bowerbird of Australia pauses at the entry to its avenuelike bower. The bird has a predilection for red and may arrange its prizes by color.

LURING ITS MATE with a cigaret package *(below)*, Australia's satin bowerbird shows its preference for blue. Often it uses its beak to paint the bower with charcoal, chewed bark and saliva.

PROFFERING A FLOWER, the golden bowerbird, smallest of the Australian species, sits on the display perch outside its maypole bower. It decorates the bower with flowers and bits of lichen.

Love Nests of the Bowerbirds

Sexual selection, which has given some male birds their dazzling plumage, has taken away most of the bright feathers of the male bowerbirds of Australia and New Guinea and substituted a remarkable behavioral pattern. Instead of wooing a mate with a proud display of finery, a bowerbird entices by building and decorating a courting area. The plainer the bowerbird, the more elaborate the bower is likely to be. The dull-hued Lauterbach often uses more than 3,000 sticks in the construction of its love nest, piles perhaps 1,000 pebbles against the walls and embellishes the bower daily with berries.

Scientists believe that at some point in the evolution of the bowerbirds—from the same stock that produced the resplendent birds of paradise—inanimate objects began to replace bright feathers as sexual stimuli. In a world of sharp-eyed predators, the toned-down male outlived its colorful brothers. This variant soon multiplied into dominance of the species, and passed on to the now relatively drab males the compensating talent of an architect-decorator.

A BONE-LITTERED PATH leads to the courting area of the spotted bowerbird, a mimic that can imitate barking dogs and galloping horses. This Australian bird collects bleached animal bones.

OVERSIZED EARS occur in many bats, which emit a stream of high-pitched squeaks while in flight, and from the echoes of these squeaks manage to avoid collisions even in pitch-dark caves. Shown above is an American species, the lump-nosed bat. The lumps on its nose and the antennalike growths in front of its ears pick up air vibrations and may improve the bat's hearing.

LIT FROM BEHIND, A BAT REVEALS A MOUSELIKE BODY AND GREATLY ELONGATED FORELEGS WHICH SUPPORT ITS WINGS OF ELASTIC SKIN

The Only Flying Mammal

A descendant of tree-dwelling insect eaters that leaped, glided and finally developed wings, the bat is now as accomplished a flyer as almost any bird. Bats occur nearly everywhere and range in size from the little bamboo bat of Southeast Asia, less than an inch and a half long, to the flying foxes of Sumatra, with five-foot wingspreads. Bats can reduce their temperature and metabolic rate while resting in the daytime, and some species hibernate through cold winters. Many live for 20 years or longer, in contrast to their relatives the rats and mice, which seldom survive more than a year or two. To compensate for this longevity, bats are slow breeders, having one or at most two babies in a year.

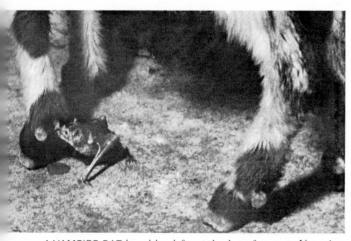

A VAMPIRE BAT laps blood from the leg of a goat. Vampires make painless incisions in the skin of animals with their sharp teeth, then sit or cling quietly, licking up the blood that flows out.

HANGING UPSIDE DOWN and looking like an umbrella blown inside out, a bat cleans its wing with its tongue. Bats sleep and hibernate in this position, sometimes in cave colonies of millions.

HUNTING PLATYPUSES, Australian zoologists wade up a shaded stream, looking for the entrances to nesting chambers. Females and males dig separate burrows, with openings just above the waterline.

The Mixed-Up Platypus

Take the fur of an otter, the tail of a beaver, the bill and webbed toes of a duck, and the spurs of a fighting cock; add them together and the sum is the platypus of Australia and Tasmania, the most bizarre of living mammals. Naturalists were fascinated by the first puzzling specimens they saw, and some even suspected a hoax: surely a faker had sewed together the unrelated parts of various animals.

But in the course of long and patient study, the platypus was finally accepted for what it is —a mammal that lays eggs but feeds its young on milk which oozes from teatless mammary

NEWLY CAUGHT, a squirming platypus (*above*) is dropped into a cage. Poison glands discharging through half-inch spurs on the hind legs of the males secrete venom similar to a rattlesnake's.

AN EXPERT SWIMMER, thanks to its webbed feet, a platypus (*right*) paddles through water in search of food. Its diet consists of snails, grubs and worms, which it roots up with its soft bill.

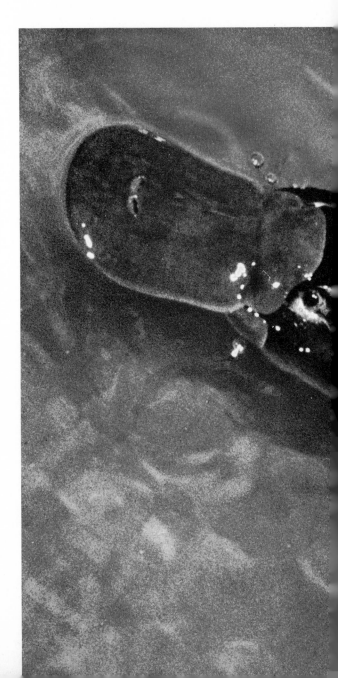

glands. It was assigned to the special order of Monotremata, a classification that it shares with only one other creature, the spiny anteater. Both of them, like reptiles, have a single ventral opening for elimination, mating and birth. Moreover, like reptiles, they have bony shoulder girdles and produce eggs that are leathery and large-yolked. The reptilian characteristics of the platypus led scientists to conclude that it is descended from a link between the reptiles and mammals of over 150 million years ago. At any rate, it is a highly specialized survivor of an ancient line.

TWO JOINED EGGS come to light when a female platypus is lifted off its leafy nest. These eggs, only three quarters of an inch long, may be stuck together to keep them from rolling around and getting lost.

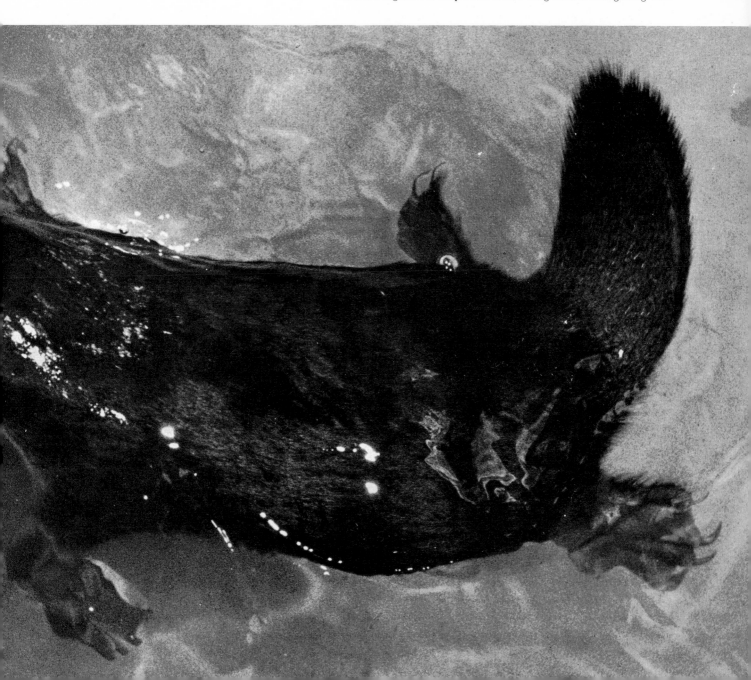

OVERLAPPING SCALES cover the giant pangolin from head to tail. Its 36-inch sticky tongue, with which it sweeps up insects, is housed in a sheath reaching from the mouth to the pelvis.

SNAPPED SHUT, the pangolin lies in a flat ball. A pad under the tail hooks over a scale on the lower back, and thus helps guard the soft belly from attack. The scales are sharp-edged.

THE LONG, POINTED QUILLS OF THE CRESTED PORCUPINE COME LOOSE

Strange Mechanisms of Defense

The armored animals on these pages look as though they were made for war, but the truth is that they are pacifists at heart. The porcupine and pangolin, however, will fight when attacked. The pangolin, whose home is Africa and southern Asia, can give an enemy a vicious swat with its heavy tail. So can the porcupine, leaving its persecutor bristling with

IN COMBAT AND WORK THEIR WAY INTO THE FLESH OF AN ATTACKER

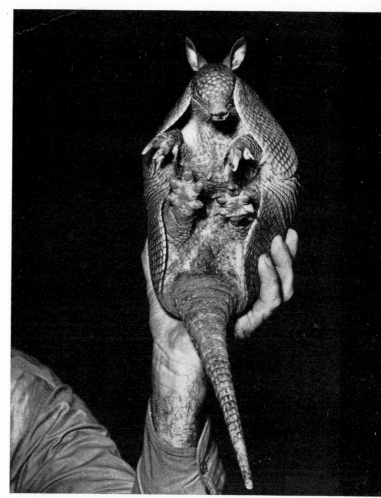

INTERLOCKING PLATES of the nine-banded armadillo hang down over its soft flanks. When in danger, armadillos dig holes to hide in, and the three-banded species roll up like pangolins.

STRETCHED OUT, an armadillo swims easily. It is fast afoot and can burrow with lightninglike speed. Darwin watched one bury itself before he could dismount from his horse to catch it.

quills. The armadillo, on the other hand, cannot even bite, and prefers to scamper from the field of battle. But without their protective coats—the gift of natural selection—these mild-tempered creatures might have been killed off long ago by predators. Today the porcupine is increasing in the northern U.S., and the armadillo is spreading in the South.

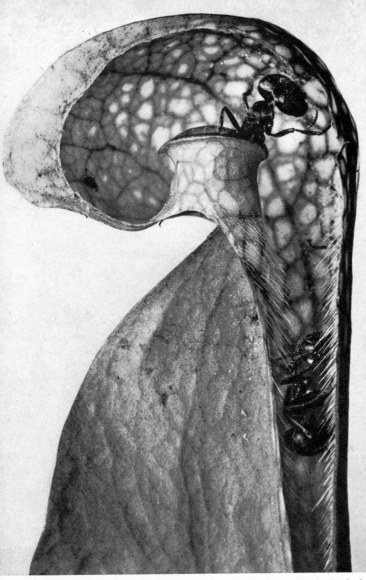

A ONE-WAY PASSAGE is followed by two ants in the leaf of a parrot pitcher plant shown in a cutaway view. Unable to back out against the slanting hairs, they will be killed and digested.

A STICKY TRAP laid by a sundew plant mires an insect on one of its leaves. The tiny hairs, tipped with gluelike globules, will close down over the victim as the process of digestion begins.

A FOUL POOL, the death-dealing instrument of a pitcher plant awaits its victim. Insects, attracted by the nectar along the rim, reach over to get the sweet substance, topple in and drown.

Plants That Eat Insects

To make up for a lack of nitrogen in the barren soil in which they grow, the strange-looking plants shown on these pages attract, capture and digest nitrogen-rich insects. They do this with the aid of highly specialized leaves, so unusual in form that some people mistake them for flowers. The fragrant leaves act as traps, snaring their insect prey either with a discharge of mechanical energy, as in the case of the Venus's-flytrap (*opposite*), or passively, as in the case of the pitcher plant (*above*).

The insectivorous plants, called *miracula naturae* (miracles of nature) by the first men who examined them, have long fascinated scientists; Darwin spent 16 years studying them. Even today many of their mysteries remain unsolved. No one knows, for example, how the Venus's-flytrap absorbs nourishment from its victims. Nor does anyone know what causes its leaf to close. Some biologists think that a release of fluid pressure near the "hinge" produces this reaction; others believe pressure in the tissue, built up by the unequal rate of growth of the leaf lobes, does it. Experiments have shown that electrical disturbances occur when the tiny hairs on the lobes are touched. Perhaps these trigger the leaf.

A BARRED CAGE, the leaf of a Venus's-flytrap incarcerates a struggling katydid. At the upper left another leaf yawns wide. Such leaves secrete a sweet-smelling fluid to draw living morsels and snap shut when the insects brush against tiny trigger hairs on the leaf surfaces. After about 10 days, during which the edible parts of the insects are absorbed, the leaves unfold again.

3

The Riddle of Heredity

For decades after the principles of evolution had been formulated, a knotty problem remained: why do living things vary, and how do the variations occur? It was at last clear that evolution functioned through the selective preservation and elimination of inherited differences between individuals. And yet no one could say how such differences came about in the first place. To complicate the problem, there seemed to be no reliable rules governing the way a given trait was handed down from parent to offspring. Often a child with black-haired parents would show up with red hair inherited from a grandparent, or even a more remote ancestor. Baffled, people fell back on the idea that heredity was somehow transmitted with the blood, and that a child bore a blend of the "bloods" of his parents. So deeply was the idea rooted that it became a part of the language—a prince of the royal blood; a blooded mare; blood will tell.

Darwin was plagued for years by this problem. In an attempt to discover how traits are inherited, he experimented with the garden pea and other plants. For all the carefulness of his work, he could never figure out the pattern or order of inheritance that he felt certain must exist. Nor, apparently, could anyone else. Darwin sedulously read many scientific journals: none of them enlightened him. No report on the discovery of the laws of heredity arrived in his mail. And yet, by an ironic coincidence, the basic laws of evolution and heredity were both developed at about the same time.

Just as Darwin was turning at last to the final formulation of the theory of evolution, an obscure Austrian monk, Gregor Johann Mendel, in 1856 launched the first of a series of experiments that were to demonstrate that inheritance, like evolution, is not a chaos or chance or miracle but a matter of law. But Darwin never heard of Mendel's work, and the monk's reports lay ignored by the scientific world for decades.

GREGOR JOHANN MENDEL

An Austrian scientist and monk (1822-1884), he discovered the basic principles of heredity through carefully controlled experiments in crossbreeding. The value of his work was not realized until 1900, more than 34 years after it was published.

MENDEL was born on July 22, 1822, in the little village of Heinzendorf in what was then Austrian Silesia and is now Czechoslovakia. His father, Anton, the owner of Peasant Holding No. 58, was known for his fine fruit trees, and he early taught young Johann how to improve them with grafts from the orchards of the local manor house.

It was a matter of pride to the Mendels that Johann did so well in his classes that he was recommended for higher schooling. But there was little money to pay his expenses and the earnest youngster had to be entered in a school at Troppau on half rations. Whenever a carrier made the trip to Troppau, Mendel's mother sent along a basket of food. Even so, he often was hungry, and worn from the constant tutoring with which he paid part of his expenses. By the time Mendel had gone on to a two-year philosophical course at the Olmütz Institute, he knew that he had better look for a profession in which he would be "spared perpetual anxiety about a means of livelihood." A teacher suggested that he enter the Augustinian monastery at Brünn. When he was accepted in 1843, Mendel gratefully took up his studies there. He assumed the name of Gregor.

From his youth Mendel, as he once said, had been "addicted to the study of Nature." In the atmosphere of the monastery he was free, as he continued his religious studies, to work on botanical experiments. In a small strip of garden Mendel began experimenting with crosses in flowers. He soon discovered that when he crossed certain varieties the same characteristics kept appearing with surprising regularity. To find out what was happening he began some experiments with white and gray mice. The books he consulted helped very little. Many studies of hybridization, the crossing of two varieties or species, had been made. The varieties that resulted seemed to follow no rule. They occurred in all sizes, colors and forms.

It struck Mendel, a student remarkably free of preconceptions, that the studies themselves had been chaotic and lacking in follow-through. No one had bred hybrids systematically for generation after generation and recorded *exactly* what individual characteristics appeared in each plant, or, in fact, worked out the kinds of experiments which would make this possible. Mendel decided to do so, realizing as he started that the experiments would have to be large enough to rule out small accidents of chance.

To begin with, he needed true-breeding plants. He also needed a plant easily protected from all foreign pollen, for if a single insect or vagrant breeze should introduce outside pollen an experiment on the inheritance of some selected character would be ruined. The legumes most nearly fulfilled his needs and after some testing Mendel chose the common garden pea for his experimental plant. The pea ordinarily fertilizes itself and is easily protected from the intrusion of outside pollen. Mendel ordered 34 varieties from seedsmen and subjected them to a two-year trial, eventually selecting 22 as suitable for his experiments.

One of Mendel's greatest assets was that he worked step by step in patient, well-disciplined ways. Instead of trying to compare plant with plant in all possible respects, a procedure that soon would have led him into a morass of difficulties, he decided to study a few easily compared pairs of characters of the pea. He selected seven:

(1) The form of the ripe seeds—round or wrinkled.
(2) The color of the peas—yellow or intense green.
(3) The color of the seed coats—gray or white.
(4) The form of the ripe pods—inflated or constricted between the seeds.
(5) The color of the unripe pods—green or vivid yellow.
(6) The positions of the flowers—axial (distributed along the stem) or terminal (bunched at the top of the stem).
(7) The length of the stem—long (six or seven feet) or short (9 to 18 inches).

Mendel was now ready to produce hybrids and he decided to start by crossing wrinkled seeds with round seeds. As soon as the buds formed on the vines, Mendel opened those of each "wrinkled" plant and pinched off the stamens to prevent the pea from producing pollen for its own fertilization. To keep any chance pollen from being carried in, he tied a little paper or calico bag around each bud. Then he collected pollen from the round-seed plants. This pollen he dusted on the stigmas of the wrinkled buds, removing their paper bags in order to do so. To settle any doubt that his results might be influenced by which plants had served as the seed parents, he also reversed the fertilizing process, dusting some of the wrinkled pollen on round buds. Mendel repeated the interchange with each of the other pairs of characteristics he was testing. Altogether he made 287 fertilizations on 70 plants.

Then he could only wait until time, sun and rain performed their work, but he finally was able to open the pods of his round-wrinkled hybrids. In them nestled only round peas. Not a wrinkled seed was to be seen. The wrinkling, a trait of half of the parents, had disappeared as completely as though it had never existed. So it was with the other six characteristics of his test plants. Although he crossed tall plants with short ones, all the offspring were tall. Although he mated yellow peas with green, the offspring were all yellow. In each of the test plots one character and only one prevailed in this first hybrid generation.

HUGO DE VRIES

He was a Dutch botanist (1848-1935) who developed the first mutation theory through extensive studies of the evening primrose. His observations of the plant's variations made him think he had formed new species through mutations.

DURING the winter, as Mendel worked with his jars of labeled pea seeds, he decided to call the character that prevailed (like roundness or yellowness) a dominant, and the one that seemingly disappeared (like wrinkledness or greenness) a recessive. Thanks to his methodical approach, he knew what had gone into his hybrids. The next step was to see what characteristics these hybrids might be hiding. To find that out he planned to let the hybrids fertilize themselves in the normal manner of peas. As soon as spring came he planted his hybrid seeds and again waited.

Once again the critical time came when the pods could be opened. Mendel broke open the first. Inside lay both round and wrinkled peas, side by side in the same pod! The "lost" wrinkling of the wrinkled grandparent had reappeared. Mendel went on to harvest 7,324 peas from his "seed form" garden. Exactly 5,474 of them were round and 1,850 wrinkled. The ratio was nearly three round to one wrinkled.

It was the same with his other test plantings. In the experiment on pea color there were three yellow peas to each green. Over-all, and ruling out a few small deviations introduced by chance, the ratio was always 3 to 1. Here was no

THE PUNNETT SQUARE

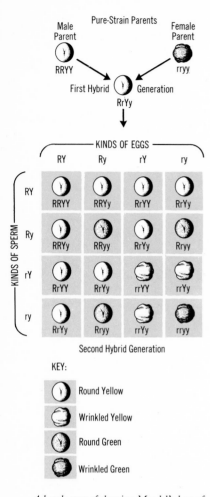

A handy way of showing Mendel's law of independent assortment of genes is the Punnett square. In the example above, a pea with two dominant characteristics of roundness and yellowness (RR and YY) is crossed with a pea having two recessive characteristics of wrinkledness and greenness (rr and yy). The hybrid that results will combine all four genes of its parents (RrYy). If hybrids are then mated, their genes will produce the different combinations shown in the square. These combinations, the square also quickly shows, result in four different-appearing kinds of peas in a ratio of 9:3:3:1.

Since two genes come from each parent, the key to using the square lies in noting the various combinations of two genes that run up the left side (one parent) and across the top (other parent). By reading in from the left and down from the top at the appropriate points, any four-gene combination can be arrived at, together with the actual appearance of the pea it represents.

haphazard recurrence of the traits of the grandparents but an exact recurrence.

But what would happen in the third generation? The next year Mendel planted his three-to-one group and again permitted each plant to fertilize itself. Now the wrinkled seeds produced only wrinkled peas, and as long as he continued to plant their descendants, through as many as seven generations, they produced only wrinkled peas.

THE story was remarkably different with the round seeds. In appearance they were all indistinguishable, but internally some were different from others. When Mendel planted them these differences appeared. Two out of three of the plants produced both round and wrinkled peas, in the ratio of 3 to 1. One out of three plants bore only round peas. Why did seemingly identical peas produce such varied descendants? With this question, Mendel began to solve the age-old riddle of heredity. The true hereditary nature of the round peas was hidden in their genetic apparatus. Some were truly round and produced only round descendants. Others merely looked round, and produced both wrinkled and round descendants. Which was which could be revealed only by planting them to see what kind of seeds they would produce. This test disclosed that two out of three rounds were actually hybrids; only one in three was a true round.

Mendel labeled the dominant characteristic "A" and the recessive one "a." When A and A came together it meant two dominants and the possibility of nothing but round peas. When a and a came together it meant two recessives and the possibility of nothing but wrinkled peas. It was only when A was combined with a to form Aa that hybrids occurred.

Mendel had concentrated up to this point on single contrasting characters. What would happen, he eventually asked, if two or more diverse characters were to be united? To see, he crossed round yellow peas with wrinkled green peas. As he anticipated, all the first-generation offspring were round and yellow—both dominant characteristics. But in the next plantings, the round yellows revealed their inner nature. As Mendel broke open the dry pods, he found in some of them four different kinds of peas: round yellow, wrinkled yellow, round green and wrinkled green.

Mendel sorted the 556 peas borne by his 15 double-hybrid plants: 315 were round yellow, 101 wrinkled yellow, 108 round green and 32 wrinkled green. The ratio was almost exactly 9:3:3:1. Then he went on to the extremely difficult experiment of crossing plants that differed in three characteristics. He crossed round yellow peas with grayish seed coats (ABC) with wrinkled green peas with white seed coats (abc). It took "time and trouble," he noted, but he obtained all the different varieties his calculations had predicted.

Charles Darwin, in his own experiments, also had obtained the three-to-one division in the hybrids. Being no mathematician, he failed to understand the significance of what he was seeing. Mendel grasped it easily. If each trait marked a separate hereditary factor, then he was obtaining every combination that could be formed. Combine A and a and only one unit could be formed, Aa. But if Aa and Aa came together, three different combinations could be made, AA, Aa and aa. Thus with one pair of hybrids three kinds of offspring would be produced; with two pairs of hybrids, nine kinds; with three, 27. The combinations would pile up three times three times three, in cubic power. In short order the possible variations could reach an astronomical number.

Mendel lacked the microscopic techniques to peer into the inner structure of his peas and search out the physical units of heredity that his experiments told him must exist. His results, however, were explainable in no other way. Mendel proceeded to formulate the biological laws that he saw must underlie his findings:

(1) Heredity is transmitted by a large number of independent, inheritable units.

(2) When each parent contributes the same kind of factor, a constant character is produced in the progeny. If each furnishes a different kind, a hybrid results, and when the hybrid forms its own reproductive cells the two different units "liberate" themselves again.

(3) The hereditary units are unaffected by their long association with others in an individual. They emerge from any union as distinct as when they entered.

Mendel himself at first regarded his findings only as hypotheses that required further testing. If he was correct though, and each hybrid pea was made up of independent hereditary units, it should be possible to prove the point by a different shuffling of the units. Two experiments would suffice.

If the hybrid AaBb, a pea round and yellow in appearance, was backcrossed with the parent plant AABB, also round and yellow-seeded, and if Mendel's theory was correct, then four combinations could be formed—AABb, AaBB, AaBb and AABB, and only the four. Since each combination would contain two dominants, all the peas would be round and yellow in appearance. Their true nature would emerge on later plantings.

Mendel made this test cross-fertilization. Much depended upon the outcome and the summer growing months were anxious ones. When the pods finally matured they contained 98 peas, every one of them round and yellow. The same experiment in reverse backcrossed the hybrid AaBb with the recessive aabb, the green wrinkled one. It went with equal precision. Mendel's calculations showed that four factor combinations should be formed—AaBb (round yellow), Aabb (round green), aaBb (wrinkled yellow) and aabb (wrinkled green)—and that all of them should appear in equal numbers.

When he harvested his peas he had 31 round yellow, 26 round green, 27 wrinkled yellow and 26 wrinkled green. As he had predicted, the ratio, allowing for small chance variations, was 1:1:1:1.

"In all the experiments," said Mendel with modest understatement, "there appeared all the forms which the proposed theory demands."

All the necessary tests had been made. The results had been predicted and nature had responded with astonishing exactness. The time had come for Mendel to publish a report on his eight years of work. During the fall and winter of 1864 he wrote the paper that would demonstrate for the first time how individual traits are transmitted from parent to offspring.

O N a frosty night in February 1865 Mendel began to read his paper before the Brünn Society for the Study of Natural Science. The members listened in unbroken silence to his discussion of the unvarying ratios in pea hybrids.

At the next meeting Mendel went on to explain what the ratios meant. The combination of mathematics and botany was an unheard-of one, and the idea that lay behind it, a vast shuffling of unseeable, unknown units, ran completely contrary to the belief that heredity was a whole or over-all matter of "blood." The minutes recorded no questions and no discussion. But Mendel was invited to prepare his paper for publication in the society's proceedings. The monk's monograph—"Experiments in Plant Hybridization"—appeared in 1866. Copies of the Brünn publication were sent as usual to more than 120 other scientific

MENDEL'S SEVEN POINTS

Mendel's pioneering observations of the pea plant were based on a comparison of the seven easily identifiable dominant and recessive characteristics illustrated below.

DOMINANT   RECESSIVE

ROUND OR WRINKLED RIPE SEEDS

YELLOW OR GREEN SEED INTERIORS

GRAY OR WHITE SEED COATS

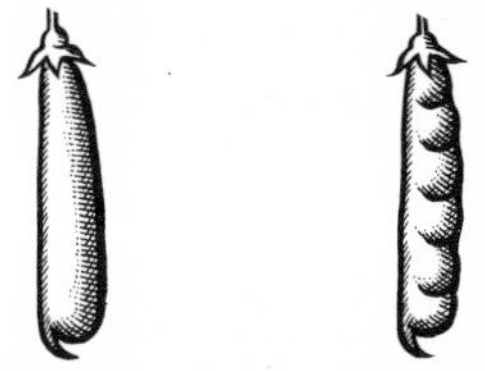

INFLATED OR PINCHED RIPE PODS

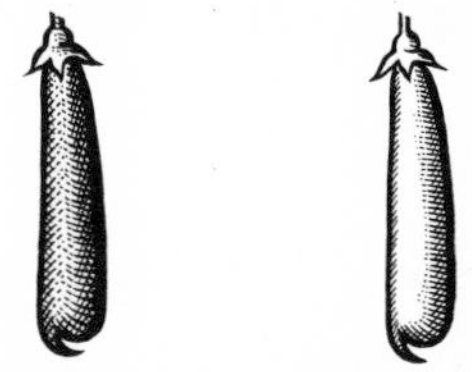

GREEN OR YELLOW UNRIPE PODS

AXIAL OR TERMINAL FLOWERS

LONG OR SHORT STEMS

organizations and universities in Europe and America. And then once more there was silence. No one praised or disputed Mendel's work, or gave it any attention at all.

Mendel made one more effort to bring it to the attention of those who might understand and appreciate it. On New Year's Eve, 1866, he wrote a carefully composed letter to Karl von Nägeli of Munich, one of the outstanding scientists of Europe. He enclosed a copy of his monograph and suggested that if Nägeli were interested in checking its conclusions he would be happy to furnish the seed. Mendel also indicated that he was thinking of doing some work with *Hieracium*, the hawkweed Nägeli had studied intensively for a number of years.

Nägeli replied several months later, commenting that Mendel's work, far from being finished, was "only beginning." He suggested that Mendel would do well to turn to the further study of the hawkweed. Mendel had raised over 10,000 hybrids and recorded his observations on 12,980 specimens, but he showed no resentment at Nägeli's patronizing comment or his obtuseness.

Pleased to have heard from the great man, Mendel undertook considerable work with the hawkweed, a plant which proved unsuitable for his work. He also tried beans. Some upsetting results began to appear. Only in certain characteristics did the flowers follow the same laws as the peas. When Mendel crossed a white-flowered, white-seeded bean with one having reddish-purple flowers and red seeds flecked with black, all of the first generation bore pale red flowers unlike either parent. In the next hybrid generation Mendel was greeted with a burst of color, from the pure white of one flower through a wide spectrum ending in reddish-purple. He was looking upon some colors that had not previously appeared in any of his test plants.

Could he have been wrong? Could an error have been made in his first results, which had shown that the first hybrid generation resembled the dominant parent? As Mendel puzzled over the in-betweenness of the pale red flowers of the first generation and the many colors of the second, it occurred to him that if the trait of color is determined in some species not by a single hereditary unit but by two such units acting together, then all of the nonconforming results could be explained. The two could produce nine variations of color. Only one ninth of the plants would bear white flowers, and eight ninths would produce almost exactly the range of color he had observed.

Mendel was working out an explanation for the in-between appearance of many offspring. It indicated that more than one hereditary unit entered into the production of certain traits. Though Mendel knew nothing of how the hereditary units might be arranged in the cell, he had come upon another of the basic laws of heredity.

THE modest monk did not dare to recognize how far he had gone. In his report to the Brünn Society, he said only that anyone studying color in plants "could hardly escape the conviction" that color too follows a definite law, but one that finds "expression in the combination of several independent color characters." He stopped with this statement. He did not admit that he had rounded out his discovery of the laws of heredity; that the whole basic pattern was there —the understanding the world had sought for centuries.

Then in 1868 Mendel was elected abbot of the monastery. At first he thought that the new post would afford wider opportunities for his work. But this proved a futile hope. Other duties pressed in on him. Soon Mendel's experiments with hybridization had to be dropped entirely. Death came to the abbot on January

6, 1884. The townspeople and civil and religious authorities gathered for the funeral of a man held in the highest esteem. But in all the gathering and indeed in the world at large, it was doubtful that anyone realized that a great scientist had gone or that his fame would be everlasting. Even his experimental notes and records disappeared.

Darwin had died two years earlier without finding the answer to the ever present problem of the evolutionary base—the variations on which natural selection acts. With the passing of the years, the problem became increasingly critical. In the 1880s Hugo de Vries, a botanist at the University of Amsterdam, was one of those asking how the variations and modifications of life come about. De Vries accepted Darwin's thesis that descent with modification is the main law of nature in the organic world. But if natural selection had only small, individual variations to act upon, how could the wide differences between species be produced?

De Vries knew that breeders could produce only limited changes when they had only small individual differences with which to work. By selecting the redder tulips in their gardens they could breed a more intensely red flower. But for a completely different shade of red they had to wait upon nature and its production of what De Vries called a mutation. Darwin had used the word "sport" for such suddenly appearing new characters, and had emphasized their importance. Some of his followers, in their all-out insistence on natural selection, tended to dismiss the effect of the sudden changes.

D E VRIES decided to watch for the occurrence of mutations. He thought that they would most likely be found in some place where a plant was adapting itself to new living conditions. One afternoon in 1886 as he walked through the countryside near Hilversum, a yellow mass of the evening primrose, *Oenothera lamarckiana*, caught his admiring eye. The tall plants with the golden flowers had recently escaped from a nearby park and were multiplying rapidly in a former potato field. De Vries hurried over to examine them closely, and saw that they varied widely. There were differences in the shape of the leaves, in the mode of branching and in the height of the plants.

De Vries decided to make a thorough study of them—and thereby launched one of the most extensive and famous of all plant studies. In the summer of 1887 as he studied the primrose plants, De Vries found 10 specimens of a new type. The 10 were growing by themselves in a corner of the field that had not been invaded by any of the other primroses. Their petals were smaller and more oval than the heart-shaped petals of the *lamarckianas*. Were they truly a new species and would they produce others of their kind? De Vries could not know until he planted their seeds. When he did they produced new plants with small, oval petals like those of the parent plant and quite unlike the petals of the *lamarckianas*. He felt certain that he had a new species and named it *Oenothera laevifolia*.

During the next decade De Vries raised or observed 53,509 primrose plants. Among them he discovered what he believed to be several new species. As he studied the data of this enormous experiment and the new plants that had appeared in the potato field or among the plantings he made in his garden, De Vries could see a pattern. The new plants always appeared full-blown. He could find no intermediates between the *lamarckianas* and the newcomers. And once the new plant had appeared it went on repeating itself; it did not revert to its ancestral form.

De Vries also noticed that the new plants did not change in all their aspects as he and most naturalists would have expected. There was no over-all alteration. On the contrary, they changed at only one or a few points. In *rubrinervis* the color of the veins turned to red and there was little other change. The flowers and the general size of the plant were unaffected, and yet it was a different plant.

If plants and other living things changed only at one or a few points, this suggested that the characters must be produced by separate hereditary units. If this were so, then each part could vary separately. Though what he had were segregated characters, not mutations, De Vries struck out boldly—and correctly: "Attributes of organisms consist of distinct, separate and independent units. These units can be associated in groups and we find, in allied species, the same units and groups of units. Transitions, such as we so frequently meet with in the external form both of animals and of plants, are as completely absent between these units as they are between the molecules of the chemist."

This was venturing onto new ground and introducing concepts completely at variance with most of the beliefs that had always been accepted. De Vries wanted to find whatever support might be available for so radical a theory. He searched the literature to see if any other naturalist had suggested that heredity was not a whole but a compound of separate units. Turning through a work on plant hybridization by a German scientist, W. O. Focke, De Vries came upon a reference to a hybridization experiment by an Austrian monk, Gregor Mendel. Focke said: "Mendel believed he had found constant numerical ratios among the types produced by hybridization."

Constant numerical ratios! This implied separate units. De Vries tracked down the reference and thus in the year 1900 discovered the work Mendel had published in 1866. On the basis of his own work, De Vries knew at once the import of what he was reading. Time and progress had at last caught up with Mendel. Until this moment De Vries had thought that he, and not an unknown monk of an earlier generation, had discovered the long-sought secrets of heredity.

LIKE Darwin confronted with Wallace's work, De Vries did not hesitate. In a paper read before the German Botanical Society on March 24, 1900, the Dutch botanist gave full credit for one of the most momentous discoveries in scientific history to the man to whom it belonged.

Coincidence again came into play. On April 24, just a month after De Vries made his disclosure, a German scientist, Karl Correns, went before the same society to tell how he too had recently found the work of Mendel. He too had been studying peas and maize, and had been encountering the constant ratios from generation to generation. He too had believed the discovery was his own.

By more coincidence a third scientist, Erich Tschermak of Vienna, had made the same discovery at the same moment. He had undertaken to repeat Darwin's experiments with peas and had found the constant ratios. On June 24, two months after Correns' report and three months after that of De Vries, Tschermak reported to the same society that he too thought he had happened upon something new until he read the work of Mendel. The remarkable triple discovery undid the neglect of decades. The simultaneous finding of Mendel's work by a Dutch, a German and an Austrian scientist and their joint confirmation of it caught the attention of the world. Mendel received the scientific acclaim that had never come in his lifetime. The world for its part gained its first true understanding of the most immediate and ancient of mysteries—how the distinctiveness and the very form of all living things are passed down from parents to offspring. The theory of evolution at last had its base.

A SEVEN-INCH MALE BLOSSOM OF THE RED TRIUMPH BEGONIA, BRED BY MAN IN THIS CENTURY, IS FLANKED BY SMALLER FEMALE FLOWERS

Man-Made Evolution

Evolution takes place most dramatically when man selects traits he likes and breeds them true in his domesticated plants or animals. In only decades he has made drab wild flowers into spectacular blooms like the one above. And in a longer time he has rung equally large changes on dogs and poultry. Thanks to Mendel, he now does scientifically what he had long done by trial and error.

75

WILD BEGONIA, one of three from which all the modern varieties below were bred, is only about the size of a 50-cent piece. It was found in 1865, growing in the Andes.

Burgeoning Begonias

By crossing the little Bolivian begonia at left with other wild varieties, horticulturists have evolved the astonishing range of begonias below—each as different in appearance as the rose, camellia or carnation it has been bred to emulate. Bringing out the genetic richness in these "mockingbird flowers" has

MARMORATA

WHITE

CAMELLIA

ROSEBUD

been made easier by the fact that begonias will grow, like potatoes, from their tubers (underground stems). This method of propagation bypasses variation and checks further change because it involves no sexual reproduction that reshuffles hereditary traits. A beautiful new kind of begonia, grown from seed, need turn up only once in a hybrid crop and it can then be duplicated endlessly through its tubers or through cuttings from the tubers' shoots. In essence, each new plant of a tuberous variety like the ones below is just one limb of an original plant —which may be growing thousands of miles away.

ORANGE

CARNATION

SUNSET

PICOTEE

CONTROLLED EVOLUTION, such as man imposes on his domesticated flowers, fruits and vegetables, becomes breathtakingly visible in the regularity and arrangement of these flowers at the Ferry-Morse Company's Flint Ranch experimental seed farm in central California. The gaudy beds in the distance are planted with sweet peas. Those in the mid-distance contain varieties of

stock. And those in the foreground hold more sweet peas, divided by bands of bachelor's-buttons. Squared off around the fragrant fields of flowers are fields of verdant onions. As one of the biggest U.S. seed producers, Ferry-Morse has farms spread across the country which turn out a trillion-odd seeds each year. Many of the seeds are types developed at the company's research farms.

THE RANGE OF ROSES runs from pure white *(lower left)* through cream and orange to red and black-red *(upper right)*—and even to new lavender shades developed since this photograph was taken. As one of the oldest domesticated plants, roses are grown everywhere from the tropics to the Arctic. In the U.S. the nurseries grow, graft and ship over 75 million rosebushes every year.

TO CROSS ROSES, hybridizers first take pollen grains from the male stamens of a flower and place them in an airtight container where they may be sealed and kept for three or four months.

TO PREPARE A MOTHER—in this case a climbing rose—the hybridizer snips off the stamens to prevent self-pollination and removes the petals to get at the female reproductive organs.

A Riot of Roses

Roses evolved some 50 million years before the emergence of man, but it is man who has brought out their present diversified loveliness. All through history poets and gardeners conducted a romance with the rose, which culminated when Napoleon's wife, the Empress Josephine, brought together the 250-odd varieties then known in Europe and began using systematic cultivation techniques similar to those shown in these pictures. Since then growers have developed over 8,000 hybrid varieties, which they then propagate sexlessly through branch buds grafted on hardy rootstocks. The two most popular roses are now hybrid teas (a complex cross of big-bloomed orientals and sturdy European types) and Floribundas (a later hybrid which has blossoms in clusters).

TO FORM SEEDS, the readied rose is dusted with pollen from the chosen male parent, leaving the grains to grow through the female style to the ovaries, where they fertilize the eggs.

TO PROTECT THE PURITY of the hybrid against further pollination by insects, each seeding flower is covered with a paper bag and cross-referenced to its case history by a number tag.

TO HARVEST SEEDS, the rose pods are picked in about five months. Only about three out of 10,000 hybrid seeds prove valuable. The finest new crosses are grafted onto hardy roots.

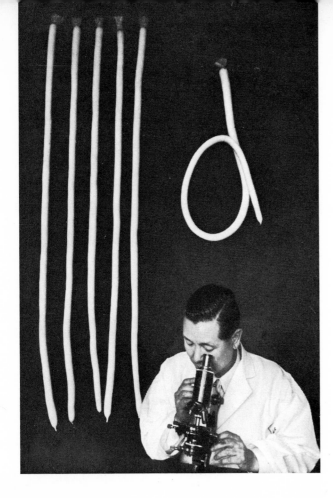

Vegetable Giants of Japan

Many farmers instinctively applied Mendel's laws before the time of Mendel, and none were more canny at it than those on the crowded islands of Japan. The Romans knew a good deal about selective breeding, but their knowledge was lost during the Dark Ages. While it was being rediscovered, Japanese gardeners, already skilled in their own ways, were developing high-yield vegetables like the radishes at left. Aided by recent scientific knowledge, Japanese botanists began furthering the farmers' efforts. Studying a rice disease—*bakanae*, or "foolish seedling," that made young plants grow too tall and fall over—they found a fungus from which they isolated one of the first plant-hormonelike substances, gibberellin. U.S. botanists have since used it to force fruits and flowers out of season and to create useful freaks like the seed cabbages on the opposite page.

FOUR-FOOT RADISHES, developed in centuries by green-thumbed Japanese farmers, hang on the wall behind a botanist who tries to find out just how the farmers did it.

FORTY-POUND RADISHES are piled up in a field on Sakurajima Island by one of a long line of shrewd farmers who have mysteriously managed to grow radishes larger than anyone else's.

BEANSTALK CABBAGES, which seed without first heading, are shown off by their breeder, Sylvan H. Wittwer. He used gibberellin, a plant chemical causing gigantism developed in Japan.

DARK CORNISH COCKEREL

BIRCHEN GAME BANTAM

FRIZZLED SULTAN ROOSTER

ONAGA-DORI COCK

PLAIN SILVER POLISH ROOSTER

BANTAM AND FULL-SIZED WHITE LEGHORN

The Pedigree and Filigree of Poultry

By 2000 B.C. the natives of northern India had brought the wild red jungle fowl *Gallus gallus*—the chicken—to a new home in the farmyard. For millennia before that they had probably kept its chicks in their hunting camps as reserve food for rainy seasons. Early poultry had wide use in augury and other tribal rituals, and it may be that ceremonial birds gave rise to flamboyant oriental cocks like the Japanese *onaga-dori* opposite. In recent times men have bred chickens for spotless eggs like those of Leghorns, or for tasty flesh like the Cornish cockerel's. But fantastic and midget breeds like the goose, duck or bantam chickens shown here are perpetuated only because fowl fanciers like them.

BLACK-TAILED JAPANESE BANTAM

CRESTED WHITE DUCK

SEBASTOPOL GOOSE

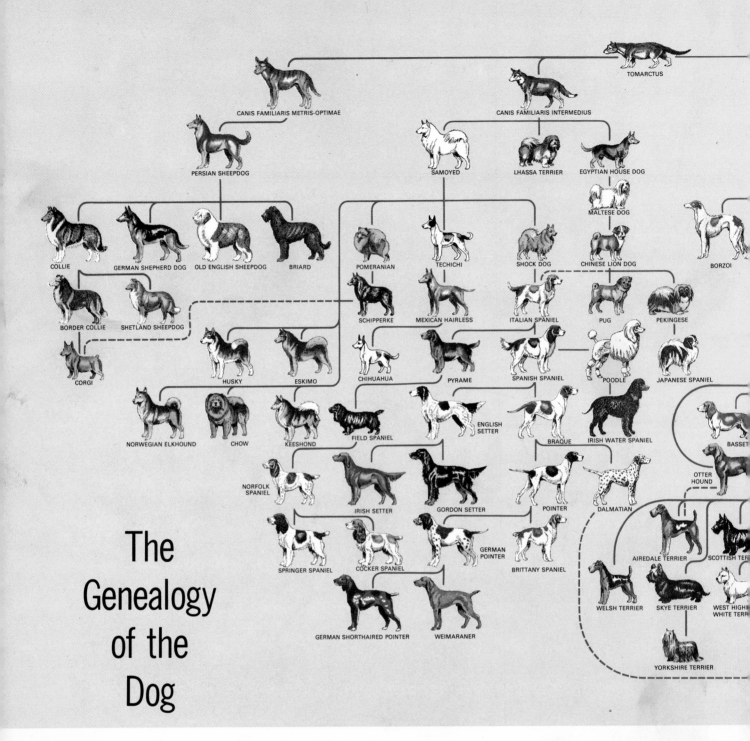

TOMARCTUS

CANIS FAMILIARIS METRIS-OPTIMAE

CANIS FAMILIARIS INTERMEDIUS

PERSIAN SHEEPDOG

SAMOYED

LHASSA TERRIER

EGYPTIAN HOUSE DOG

MALTESE DOG

COLLIE

GERMAN SHEPHERD DOG

OLD ENGLISH SHEEPDOG

BRIARD

POMERANIAN

TECHICHI

SHOCK DOG

CHINESE LION DOG

BORZOI

BORDER COLLIE

SHETLAND SHEEPDOG

SCHIPPERKE

MEXICAN HAIRLESS

ITALIAN SPANIEL

PUG

PEKINGESE

CORGI

HUSKY

ESKIMO

CHIHUAHUA

PYRAME

SPANISH SPANIEL

POODLE

JAPANESE SPANIEL

NORWEGIAN ELKHOUND

CHOW

KEESHOND

FIELD SPANIEL

ENGLISH SETTER

BRAQUE

IRISH WATER SPANIEL

BASSET

NORFOLK SPANIEL

IRISH SETTER

GORDON SETTER

POINTER

DALMATIAN

OTTER HOUND

SPRINGER SPANIEL

COCKER SPANIEL

GERMAN POINTER

BRITTANY SPANIEL

AIREDALE TERRIER

SCOTTISH TER

GERMAN SHORTHAIRED POINTER

WEIMARANER

WELSH TERRIER

SKYE TERRIER

WEST HIGH
WHITE TERR

YORKSHIRE TERRIER

The Genealogy of the Dog

The modern domestic dog is descended from the same mammalian stock that produced bears, raccoons, cats, hyenas and seals. The prototype dog was *Tomarctus*, shown at the top of this chart. It was a short-legged predator that lived 15 million years ago and probably also gave rise to wolves and jackals, but not to foxes, dholes and other doglike creatures which, despite apparent resemblances, belong to separate genera. True dogs belong to the genus *Canis*, comprising eight species, all but one

of which are wild. The single, domesticated exception is man's friend, *Canis familiaris*, which, though capable of interbreeding with its wild brethren, seldom does so. Instead it has been developed, in a process of highly unnatural selection, into an assortment of shapes, colors, sizes and personalities suited to man's needs.

The four great cleavages in canine genealogy appeared prehistorically in the prototype breeds shown directly under *Tomarctus* above. From *metris optimae*

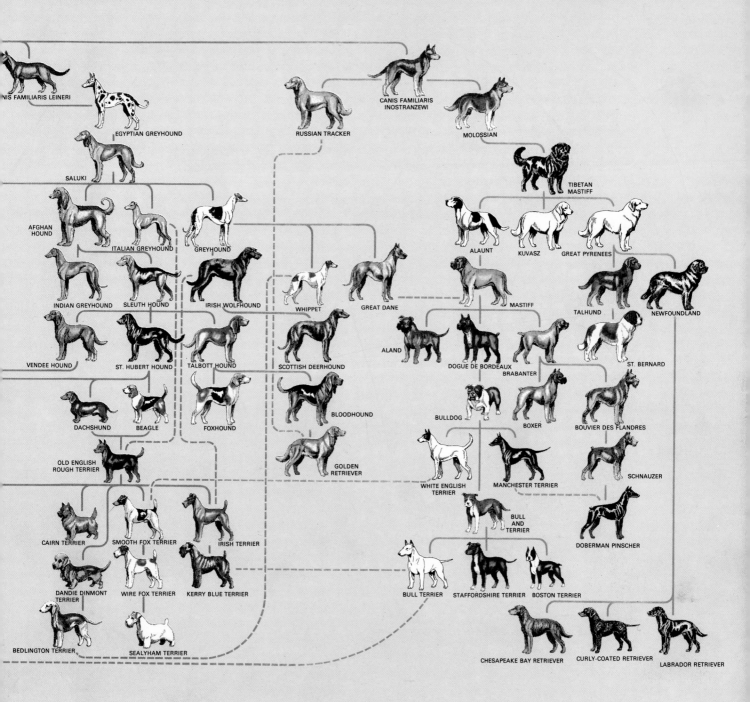

NIS FAMILIARIS LEINERI

EGYPTIAN GREYHOUND

RUSSIAN TRACKER

CANIS FAMILIARIS INOSTRANZEWI

MOLOSSIAN

SALUKI

TIBETAN MASTIFF

AFGHAN HOUND

ITALIAN GREYHOUND

GREYHOUND

ALAUNT

KUVASZ

GREAT PYRENEES

INDIAN GREYHOUND

SLEUTH HOUND

IRISH WOLFHOUND

WHIPPET

GREAT DANE

MASTIFF

TALHUND

NEWFOUNDLAND

VENDEE HOUND

ST. HUBERT HOUND

TALBOTT HOUND

SCOTTISH DEERHOUND

ALAND

DOGUE DE BORDEAUX

ST. BERNARD

BRABANTER

DACHSHUND

BEAGLE

FOXHOUND

BLOODHOUND

BULLDOG

BOXER

BOUVIER DES FLANDRES

OLD ENGLISH ROUGH TERRIER

GOLDEN RETRIEVER

WHITE ENGLISH TERRIER

MANCHESTER TERRIER

SCHNAUZER

CAIRN TERRIER

SMOOTH FOX TERRIER

IRISH TERRIER

BULL AND TERRIER

DOBERMAN PINSCHER

DANDIE DINMONT TERRIER

WIRE FOX TERRIER

KERRY BLUE TERRIER

BULL TERRIER

STAFFORDSHIRE TERRIER

BOSTON TERRIER

BEDLINGTON TERRIER

SEALYHAM TERRIER

CHESAPEAKE BAY RETRIEVER

CURLY-COATED RETRIEVER

LABRADOR RETRIEVER

developed smart sheep dogs and collies. From *inter-medius* came the tractable, hard-working, fetching type of hunting and work dogs—Huskies, chows, Pekingese, Chihuahuas, setters and spaniels. From *leineri* sprang the sleek, fleet hounds and terriers used for running quarry down—whippets, bassets, beagles, great Danes, dachshunds, greyhounds and fox terriers. From *inostranzewi* descended heavy-jawed, holdfast bulldogs, mastiffs, Newfoundlands, boxers, bull terriers, Labradors and Chesapeakes.

In the development of the 110 separate breeds shown here—and recognized as breeds in modern dog shows—the four ancestral subspecies have not remained entirely distinct. New strains have often been helped along by mongrelization, as indicated by the dotted lines. The fact that dogs of the four different groups can still interbreed proves that they really are all one species—but one of a diversity which shows how far selective crossbreeding can carry the descendants of a single genetic stock.

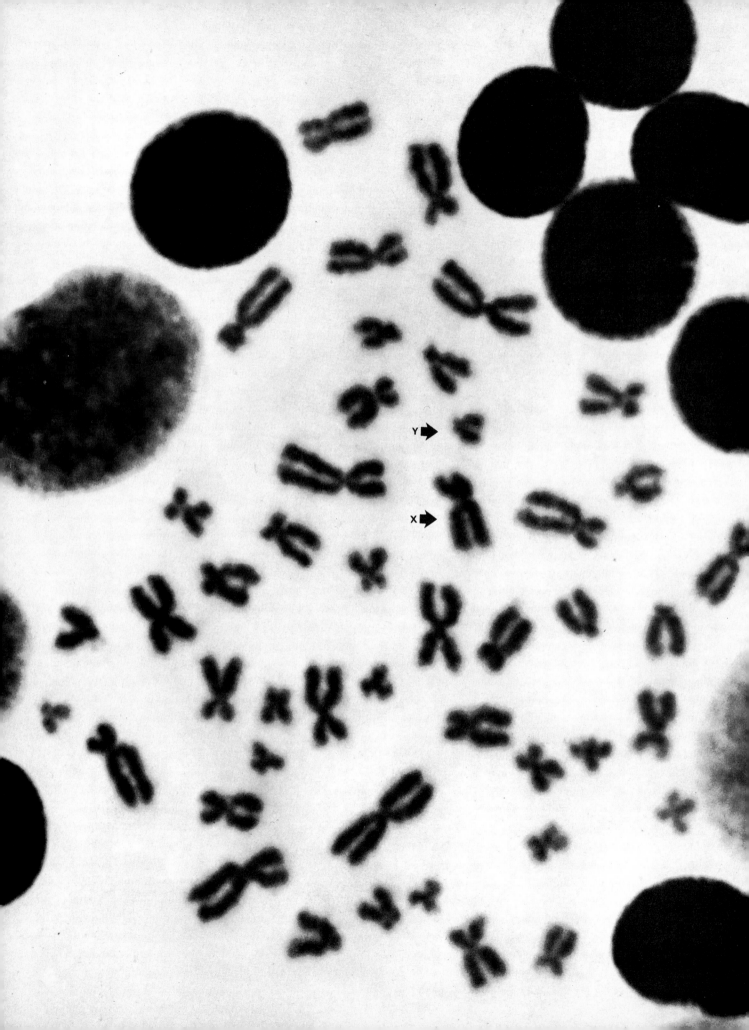

4

Chromosomes, Genes and DNA

A MILLION animal species and a quarter million kinds of plants inhabit the world today, and yet they are only a fractional measure of life's vast capacity for coming up with something different, for millions of others have evolved, flourished and become extinct. Darwin gave them all a common ancestry and Mendel found that law, not anarchy, governs their descent. But Darwin and Mendel raised more questions for the 20th Century than they answered for the 19th. If separate hereditary units accounted for all the differences in the forms of life, what *were* these units? Where were they hidden away in living tissues? How did they work in producing the differences they created? Could man ever control them? The search for the answers has brought science close to the ultimate secrets of life, has given rise to whole new scientific disciplines and has been punctuated by a great deal of argument among scientists.

It seemed to De Vries, the primrose scholar, that evolution could never get anywhere by natural selection alone. To him the sudden fits and starts which he called mutations (and whose results he was overeager to label as new species) were the chief force in pushing things along. Natural selection, he argued, is not a force of nature, but only a sieve deciding which is to live and which is to die. It has nothing to do with the single steps of evolution; only after a step has been taken does the sieve act. It was clear to him that different kinds of things —mutants—have to be put in the sieve before it can make a selection.

The Darwinians battled back: natural, gradual selection is everything, they said, and the large, sudden mutations in species are meaningless in evolution's long run. De Vries retorted that "the general belief in slow changes has held back science during half a century." The battle became fierce. The mutationists for a time thought they had found their incontrovertible proof in the phenomenon of mimicry. In the Orient, for example, there lives a handsomely marked butterfly, *Danaida tytia*. Its grayish upper wings are patterned in a strong tracery of black, while its lower wings are exquisitely etched in brown.

In some of *Danaida's* territory, the butterfly *Papilio agestor* also lives. Its wings bear the same coloring and markings and are even the same shape, though they are slightly wider than *Danaida's*. In every way *Papilio* is an excellent mimic of *Danaida*. The latter has another mimic in southwest China. Here *Neptis imitans* is just as close a replica, with the same striking colors and designs. Even a careful observer—or a careless bird—may mistake the mimics for *Danaida*. And this is the point of the mimicry. For all its delicate appearance *Danaida* is a tough, rubbery insect. Naturalists have seen it flutter away unharmed after being seized and distastefully dropped by a bird. So the birds avoid *Danaida*. On the other hand, *Papilio* and *Neptis* are tender morsels. They have found safety in mimicry of unpalatable *Danaida:* the more they resemble it, the better their chance to escape being eaten.

Studying such wondrous resemblances, the mutationists decided that they could have arisen only by mutation. How else could an elaborate design on the gossamer wing of a butterfly come into being? Mimicry, they said, is the outstanding proof of mutation, or the "discontinuous" origin of species.

The dispute was a standoff until such men as Sir Ronald Aylmer Fisher, J.B.S. Haldane and the American geneticist Sewell Wright entered the fray with a new weapon, mathematics. Such things as hereditary units, change, degrees of difference and alterations in natural populations were all subject to mathematical analysis and test. Fisher, a statistician, mathematician and later professor of genetics at Cambridge, brought mathematical analysis to bear on the mutationists' pet phenomenon of mimicry. His calculations showed that only natural selection could bring about such intricate adaptations as the matching of mimic to model. The double occurrence of such insect patterns and shapes by the randomness of mutation was so unlikely as to be mathematically impossible.

Nor could mutation explain the proximity of model and mimic, which are always found in the same regions and in the same season. Often *Danaida* and its imitators are captured flying together. If their similarities had arisen by mutation, why should not the same patterns have occurred in other butterflies in other places? Fisher also pointed out that the copycat looks no more like the copied species than necessary. Beneath the obvious, eye-deceiving colorings, shapes and movements, model and mimic are as unlike as any two species.

AFTER additional proofs confirmed Fisher's findings, mutation tumbled from the place De Vries had given it as evolution's prime agent. Natural selection was unequivocally assigned the main role, and mutation a supplementary role. But if mutation alone could no longer be given credit for the amazing adaptations of the natural world and hence for evolution, the researches showed that it at least supplied the raw material for these changes. For

THOMAS HUNT MORGAN

An American biologist (1866-1945) and Nobel Prizewinner, Morgan is the father of modern genetics. His pioneer studies among the fast-breeding fruit flies eventually led to many improvements in agricultural techniques and animal breeding.

without the new opportunities produced by mutations, life would sink into a rut. It would be unprepared to cope with such constant changes in physical environment as ice ages, long droughts, and the slow elevations and subsidences of the earth's crust, or such changes in the living environment as the appearance of a swifter foe, a deadlier germ, or an adversary equipped with a gun.

"The function of mutation," wrote Fisher, "is to maintain the stock of genetic variance at a high level." But if this analysis was right, some seeming contradictions had to be resolved. Work in many laboratories was showing that most mutations are detrimental and the most drastic ones are usually lethal. They are steps in the wrong direction in the sense that any change in a smooth-running, well-adjusted organism is likely to be for the worse. Most bearers of radical mutations never survive long enough to pass the changes along to offspring. This being so, can mutations build up a "stock" for variation?

The fact is that while a big change in round peg or square hole is fatal, a tiny change or adjustment may improve the fit. Thus a few mutations, generally small ones, prove beneficial to species. So the next question for the geneticists was: how can a rare, tiny, beneficial change—say a change in bone structure that makes a fin of a fish potentially usable as a leg—spread through a large species? Will it not be swamped in the ordinary mating of two individuals and, later, their descendants? Not at all, said the mathematicians. Let us assume a mutation that would have an advantage of only 1 per cent over the organism from which it arose. A percentage that small would mean the survival of 100 mutants as against 99 unmutated individuals. Then, in a short time as evolution goes, the mutant would replace the original as the population's normal type. While harmful or at best useless mutations may crop up, vanish and reappear in a species, most with predictable frequency, the ones which ultimately pervade a species and become part of its normal make-up are mostly beneficial.

HERMANN J. MULLER

Another American Nobel Prize-winning geneticist, Muller (1890-   ) also worked with common fruit flies. He subjected the insects to X rays and other forms of radiation, creating a host of mutations by damaging the genes on their chromosomes.

To Fisher, the great contrast between abundant species and rare ones lay in the fact that an abundance of individuals meant an abundance of possible mutations—hence more possibilities for adapting to new conditions. With fewer possible mutants to help it cope with changes in the environment, a small species might face a dwindling future. But a numerous species such as man was likely to have a varied enough genetic "pool" to meet almost any change that might confront it. If a species had only 100 characteristics that could exist in two forms, he figured, more than 1,000,000,000,000,000,000,000,000,000,000 genetic combinations were possible when two of its members produced offspring. Mendel's conclusion that the number of combinations would increase in mathematical ratio was amply borne out. Evolution, both Fisher and Haldane realized, could head off in many directions and along tangents no one could conceive.

"It has often been remarked, and truly, that without mutation evolutionary progress, whatever direction it may take, will ultimately come to a standstill for lack of further possible improvements," Fisher commented. "It has not so often been realized how far most species must be from such a state of stagnation, or how easily, with no more than one hundred factors a species may be modified to a condition considerably outside the range of its previous variation. . . ." With equations stretching across pages of his book, *Genetical Theory of Natural Selection*, Fisher proved that this richness of genetic variability is directly related to fitness for survival. What counted was not the plant struggling against the drought or the rabbit eluding the fox, but the nature and the preservation of the genetic material that made it possible for the plant species or the

HOW CELLS DIVIDE

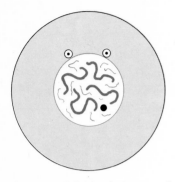

Mitosis, or cell division, is the process by which one cell splits into identical twins, and it requires an elaborate mechanism for dividing and separating the chromosomes. In the first stage of mitosis, the chromosomes become prominent in the nucleus.

As the coiled chromosomes continue to thicken by absorbing chemicals from the cell, a halo of fibers, called the spindle, begins to grow across the cell from a pair of star-shaped figures, or asters. Later, the chromosomes use this spindle as a ladder.

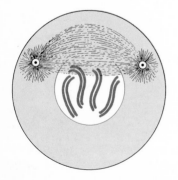

The number of fibers in the spindle increases as the chromosomes start to replicate themselves by dividing lengthwise. The wall of the nucleus is now ready to break down and permit the chromosomes to escape toward opposite ends of the cell.

rabbit species to win out. Evolution was the evolution of the mysterious, almost infinitely variable hereditary units whose existence Mendel had inferred.

Mendel had no way to inquire into what such units might be, or where they might be located within the living cell. But in the years when his monographs were sitting unread and unknown on library shelves, scientists discovered a number of tiny, threadlike structures in the nucleus of the cell. When stained they could be seen under a microscope. Close observation revealed that they went through remarkable maneuvers. When a cell was about to divide they split in two and moved out to opposite ends of the cell. A cell wall grew between them, and in an hour, more or less, there were two cells where there had been only one. Each was equipped with a full, identical set of these chromosome threads. But when a new egg or sperm cell was to be formed, the maneuvers differed. Only half of each set of chromosome pairs went into the new sex cell. Thus when a new individual was created by the fertilization of egg by sperm, the full chromosome complement was re-established, half of it coming from each parent.

IT was in 1902, two years after Mendel's work came to light, that W. S. Sutton of Columbia University suggested that the chromosomes might be the containers of Mendel's hereditary units. In their coming together and pulling apart, they supplied just the kind of mechanism needed to produce Mendel's results. A few years later William Bateson and R. C. Punnett, experimenting with sweet peas, crossed a purple-flowered plant with a long pollen grain and a red-flowered, round-grained plant. Instead of obtaining the free assortment of characters that Mendel found in garden peas, these English researchers found that the red flower and the round pollen grain tended to stay in indissoluble association. Other investigators came upon the same phenomenon. Certain traits seemed to be coupled—perhaps controlled by the same chromosome.

Thomas Hunt Morgan of Columbia University was one of those finding the same kind of associated linkages. They kept cropping up in the fruit flies, *Drosophila melanogaster*, with which he was working. In 1910, about a year after he began studying the little flies that orbit around ripe fruit, a fly with white eyes appeared in one of the milk bottles he used for incubators. Since the wild flies have red eyes, he felt certain that this was a mutation. He bred the white-eyed male to a red-eyed female and in a short time had hundreds of red-eyed offspring, just as the Mendelian laws would lead him to expect. To bring out their underlying heredity, Morgan then bred red-eyed hybrids to red-eyed hybrids. The matings produced 50 per cent red-eyed females, 25 per cent red-eyed males, 25 per cent white-eyed males—but not one white-eyed female. By all indications the hereditary unit for white eyes, the mutated unit, was linked to the sex chromosome—assuming of course that the chromosomes were in fact the bearers of heredity.

It was obvious to Morgan "that there was one essential requirement for the chromosome view, namely that all factors carried by the same chromosome should tend to remain together." The fruit fly had four pairs of chromosomes. If Morgan was right, it should be possible to "map" the hereditary factors carried by each and he set out to do it. It took nearly 17 years and the breeding of millions of flies, but in the end Morgan and the "fly squad" of young scientists working with him found that there were very precise locations on the chromosomes that controlled specific characteristics in a fly. Ultimately actual chromosome maps were made: long vertical lines on which were marked the sites of "yellow body, white eyes, echinus eyes, cross veinless, cut wing, vermilion eyes, miniature wing, sable body, garnet eyes, forked bristles, bar eyes, clipped wing and bobbed bristles." These were the descriptive names for the physical characteristics of the different flies, characteristics whose determinant factors had been narrowed down to specific locations on their chromosomes. These determining units were given the name genes.

Often, however, a whole group of genetic units was involved in producing a single characteristic, such as the color of a stem or the weight of a fowl. In one experiment a race of fowl weighing an average of 1,300 grams was bred to a race of bantams whose weight averaged 750 grams. The offspring tended to split the difference in weight, but when hybrid was bred to hybrid there was a "wild outburst" of variation, ranging from monstrous birds of 1,700 grams down to some tinier than the bantam grandparents. J.B.S. Haldane estimated that if 10 genes affected weight, they could combine in enough ways to produce 59,049 different weights. In effect the variation would be continuous.

In all these painstaking research projects, says Sir Julian Huxley, biologist grandson of the Thomas Huxley who was Darwin's stanch defender, two most important things were established. One was that inheritance is particulate—that it operates through the transmission of definite bits of self-producing matter. The other was that it is cooperative—that the hereditary particles, or genes, "combine or interact to produce their effects, all being organized in a single functional system, the gene complex. With this realization, not only did genetics find a firm scientific base, but the relations between genetics and evolution were put on a new and satisfactory footing."

But all the same, what *was* a gene, and what happened when a gene mutated? If mutations could be induced and their changes studied, something might be learned about the structure of these "bits of self-reproducing matter." Many scientists worked on the problem. In efforts to force changes in the submicroscopic units deep in the nucleus of the cell, they tried heat, cold, drugs, poison and even mutilation. But genes were too tough and stable to be altered by such tampering. Then H. J. Muller, who had begun his scientific work as one of Morgan's "fly squad," got to wondering if mutation might be brought about by ultramicroscopic forces. X rays, he knew, are agents capable of striking one minute point with drastic effect while bypassing another point a thousandth of a millimeter away. Mutations occurred at just such pin-point ranges.

So Muller put hundreds of fruit flies in gelatin capsules and bombarded them with X rays. The irradiated flies were then bred to untreated ones. In 10 days thousands of their offspring were buzzing around their banana-mash feed, and Muller was looking upon an unprecedented outburst of man-made mutations. There were flies with bulging eyes, flat eyes, purple, yellow and brown eyes. Some had curly bristles, some no bristles. There were flies with broad wings or downturned wings or almost no wings at all. "They were a motley throng," said Muller. "The results of these experiments were startling and unequivocal. The roots of life—the genes—had indeed been struck and they had yielded." And Muller's work with them won him a Nobel Prize.

T HE genes had yielded some secrets of their mechanics, but their chemistry remained inscrutable. Through most of the years while Mendel and Morgan were tracing the effects of heredity's units, and while Haldane, Fisher and Wright were establishing the genetic basis for the theory of evolution—as the sum of the continuous changing and recombining of these units—bottles of a white powder were sitting on the shelves of many laboratories. This powder was

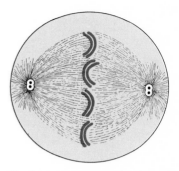

The chromosomes are now aligned in pairs and have become attached to the spindle. They are ready to migrate along its fibers. The nucleus has disappeared completely and the cores of the asters, called centrioles, have also divided into separate pairs.

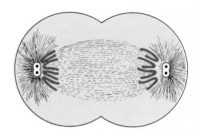

Chromosome migration is under way, with one of each pair moving along the spindle fibers toward the edges of the cell. By this time the cell itself is ready to split, and becomes pinched in at the middle. The spindle begins to disintegrate.

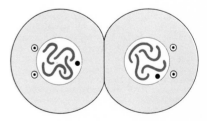

Having done its job of moving the chromosomes, the spindle disappears completely. Meanwhile the pinching process continues until two cells exist where one did before, each with a complete set of chromosomes, two centrioles and its own nucleus.

THREE KINDS
OF ASEXUAL REPRODUCTION

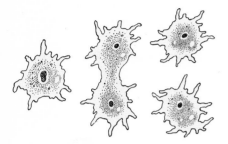

The amoeba, one of the simplest forms of animal life, reproduces by splitting in two, as shown in the drawing above. The single-celled offspring is always identical with the parent, since in asexual reproduction there is no mingling of genes.

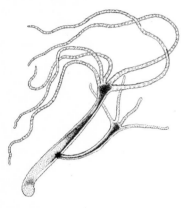

The hydra, a tiny fresh-water animal, reproduces by budding. The bud, growing from the cellular wall of the "mother," will eventually break away and mature on its own. And like the amoeba, it will be an exact genetic echo of the parent.

The leaf of a bryophyllum puts out tiny plants of its own, complete with roots— another example of budding in asexual reproduction. When the leaf falls to the ground, the plants grow. The bryophyllum can also reproduce sexually by seed.

labeled nucleic acid. A Swiss chemist named Friedrich Miescher had discovered it in 1869 while breaking down some cells. The cells disintegrated but part of their nuclei remained intact, and when analyzed this remainder was found to differ chemically from all other known cellular material.

In time other scientists found that the acid had a threadlike structure and that its molecules were huge. They also learned that it occurred only in chromosomes. Its chemical composition was worked out and the powder was renamed deoxyribonucleic acid, or DNA for short. Later a second nucleic acid was found, differing only slightly from DNA. It was called RNA, for ribonucleic acid. There the matter rested; the bottles continued to sit on laboratory shelves.

By the 1940s it was clear that the answer to the form and functioning of life had to be sought in the materials out of which chromosomes were made. These were essentially two, DNA and protein. A brilliant series of experiments at the Biological Laboratory, Cold Spring Harbor, New York, showed that when a virus, acting much like a physician's syringe, shot its DNA contents into a bacterial cell, the DNA took command. In 24 minutes it produced complete copies of itself. The virus's protein shell, comparable to the casing of the syringe, had been left on the outside of the cell wall. All that entered the cell was the DNA, and it produced not only new DNA but new protein overcoats for the new viruses as well. All the directives for building more DNA and more protein were encompassed in the DNA or in its near-copy, the RNA. This, then, was the long-sought raw material of heredity, the basic stuff of life and of evolution.

Here was a bit of matter too small to be detected in the cell except under the tremendous enlarging power of the electron microscope, yet so omniscient that it could embody all the instructions needed for the building of a new virus or a beetle or a man. All DNA was made of the same materials: nucleotides composed of four bases, called adenine, thymine, cytosine and guanine (and known as A, T, C and G), plus some sugar molecules and a kinky phosphate molecule joining the sugar pieces. Therefore the secret of its marvels of creative diversity had to be sought not in its composition but in its structure. Something in the way DNA was built had to account for the billions of forms it could command.

In the 1950s the trackdown of this secret began in laboratories all over the world. At the Cavendish Laboratory at Cambridge, F.H.C. Crick and James D. Watson, a young American working with him, fashioned a wire model which portrayed DNA as a helix, looking like a spiral staircase. The sugars and the phosphate were the framework, and the four nucleotide bases, A, T, C and G, were strung around it like four kinds of repeated steps.

The 46 human chromosomes, H. J. Muller estimated, contain some four billion of these bases, or steps. If each one were written down as a single alphabetical letter, they would fill 100 large dictionaries—a sort of code, defining man. The order of such steps is different for each living thing; it is the endless variety of their order that explains the limitless variety of the living world. The long coils of DNA have a property uniquely their own—their capacity for reproducing or replicating themselves. At the right time for self-replication, the staircase divides down the middle. From free nucleotide units in the cell nucleus, each half-step, or base, picks up another unit complementary to itself, and a new coil is formed.

In November 1959 the world's leading authorities on evolution met at the University of Chicago to celebrate the centennial of the publication of *The Origin of Species* and to discuss "Evolution after Darwin." Many of them spoke in the new terms of DNA. New definitions had to be forged and given, for life now was seen to hang by a thread: it "appears to depend on self-replicating and self-varying (mutating) strings of DNA, and these self-replicating and self-varying properties inevitably lead to natural selection."

How fine these DNA variations might be, and how far-reaching their effects, became apparent as research progressed. At first the secret of how DNA works its marvels had to be studied by working backward. At a dinner of scientists, a physician fell to discussing sickle-cell anemia. In this disease of the human blood, he said, red cells are twisted into a sickle shape in the venous blood of a patient (where the cells are low in oxygen), but resume their normal globular form when the blood passes through the lungs, regaining oxygen, and enters the arteries. A few sickle cells make little difference, but a person who inherits a high percentage of them gets a serious, sometimes fatal anemia. Linus Pauling, Nobel Prizewinner of the California Institute of Technology, listened to all this with excitement. He was not familiar with sickle-cell anemia, but as a chemist he knew that the only parts of the red cells that are concerned in the regular taking-on and giving-up of oxygen are the hemoglobin molecules—100 million of them to a cell. "The idea burst upon me," he said, "that the molecules of hemoglobin in the red cells might be responsible for the disease—that the disease might be a molecular one involving an abnormal sort of hemoglobin manufactured by the patient because of the possession of abnormal genes in place of the normal genes that control the manufacture of normal hemoglobin."

Pauling's insight proved to be correct. Vernon M. Ingram of Cambridge University decided to trace the sickle-cell disease back to its DNA source. He first had to find what part of the hemoglobin molecule, a huge one with 8,000 atoms, was altered. This was a stupendous task, for the molecule is made up of some 300 amino acids of 19 different kinds. By breaking up a sickle-cell hemoglobin molecule and a normal one and comparing them, Ingram learned that they differed only at one point, which he called the "Number Four spot." This spot in normal cells includes two units of glutamic acid and one of valine. The sickle cells include the reverse, one unit of glutamic acid and two of valine.

Ingram reported, "the sole chemical difference is that in the abnormal molecule a valine is substituted for glutamic acid at one point. A change of one amino acid in nearly 300 is certainly a very small change indeed, and yet this slight change can be fatal to the unfortunate possessor of the errant hemoglobin."

BUT why was one amino acid changed? The question involved the problem of how DNA assembles the amino acids into proteins and, beyond that, how like begets like. At this point the scientists had in part to theorize. Assuming that DNA was organized in the helix, or spiral-staircase, form, Ingram and his associate John Hunt drew up a diagram showing how the four bases, A, T, C and G, might be arranged in one section to capture the normal amino acid—glutamic—for the normal hemoglobin. It read like this:

$$
\begin{array}{ll}
\text{C} & \text{G} \\
\text{T} & \text{A} \\
\text{G} & \text{C}
\end{array}
$$

Normally, C is always paired with G, and T with A. But if a mutation replaced the T—A pairing with a G—C pairing, the mutated DNA line-up would be:

$$
\begin{array}{ll}
\text{C} & \text{G} \\
\text{G} & \text{C} \\
\text{G} & \text{C}
\end{array}
$$

Because they produce very few young, the higher animals must protect them during early development. A chick embryo (above) is shielded for three weeks inside a strong shell, with its own food supply. When it hatches it can see, and takes care of itself.

Marsupials, like the kangaroo, are born blind, deaf, hairless and completely helpless except for claws and an instinct to suckle. At birth they crawl into the mother's pouch, attach themselves to her nipples and remain there for at least four months.

Mammals guard their embryos during development, carrying them in their wombs. At their birth they are helpless and must be cared for by their mothers for varying lengths of time. The longest childhood besides man's is the elephant's—10 years.

95

and valine would be captured—exactly the amino-acid substitution that causes sickle-cell anemia.

A mutation in DNA thus may be a change in a single nucleotide, or "step." In greatly simplified terms it is the line-up of the DNA, whether normal or mutated, that dictates the order of amino acids in the protein; this in turn dictates the "shape" and hence the specific activity of the proteins; and protein activity dictates the forms of all living things. Or, to put it into numbers, the four bases of DNA arrange 20 universal amino acids in patterns forming the thousands of proteins that control life's infinite variety.

Now scientists could draw up a code indicating how the four "steps" could assemble the 20 universal amino acids, but until 1961 the code was purely theoretical. Then Marshall Nirenberg of the National Institutes of Health broke the code for one amino acid. He was working with that RNA which is a near-replica of DNA and which moves out of the cell nucleus into the cell's outer part, or cytoplasm, and does the actual work of producing the proteins. DNA, like an architect's master plan, is preserved and guarded while RNA, like a blueprint, is used for the everyday work. But RNA, in the not wholly explained course of its production, acquires a unit of uracil in place of DNA's thymine step; its initials are thus A, U, C and G instead of DNA's A, T, C and G.

Nirenberg found that whenever three units of uracil, or U, succeed one another in the RNA line-up, a protein made entirely of the amino acid phenylalanine is assembled. This was UUU, one unit of the code; there were 19 more amino acids to go. In less than six months Nirenberg had the RNA composition worked out for 15 of the amino acids, and shortly Severo Ochoa of New York University, a Nobel Prizewinner of 1959, announced the code for all 20. But except for UUU, the exact *order* of the nucleotide steps in each of the acids was not certain. It was as though a researcher knew that the word "cat" is composed of the three letters c, a and t, but had not yet determined their right order.

Science at this point was on the brink of learning all about how DNA performs its orderly wonders, and was not far from learning how to interpret the exact order of some specific DNA structure, perhaps at first the relatively short coil structures of a virus. Beyond—perhaps far beyond—lay the possibility of understanding, and dealing with, the misarrangements of DNA that produce such hereditary diseases as sickle-cell anemia. Still farther ahead lay the prospect that man might alter the aberrant order of DNA that causes cancer or defective mentality. Even the physical course of evolution might be influenced—perhaps.

SCIENCE does not by any means dismiss such stirring possibilities. All of life, it became apparent in 1961, is not only built from the same basic DNA units, but is also assembled by one kind of process, or code. For in that year Dr. Fritz Lipmann of the Rockefeller Institute, another Nobel Prizewinner, replaced transfer RNA in rabbit hemoglobin with transfer RNA from a foreign body—a bacterium found in human intestines—without destroying the normal function of protein formation in the rabbit hemoglobin. It hardly would be more amazing for a cat to give birth to a fish, or a plant to puppies. And yet it was not so strange. The common denominator already had been found, the basic units that Mendel had hypothesized, and their basic plan of assembly. The code, by all indications, was universal. No more striking proof of life's own universality had been adduced since Darwin provided the living world with one immemorial pedigree. The universality of the self-replicating, self-varying genetic material, DNA, testified conclusively to the oneness of life and its evolution.

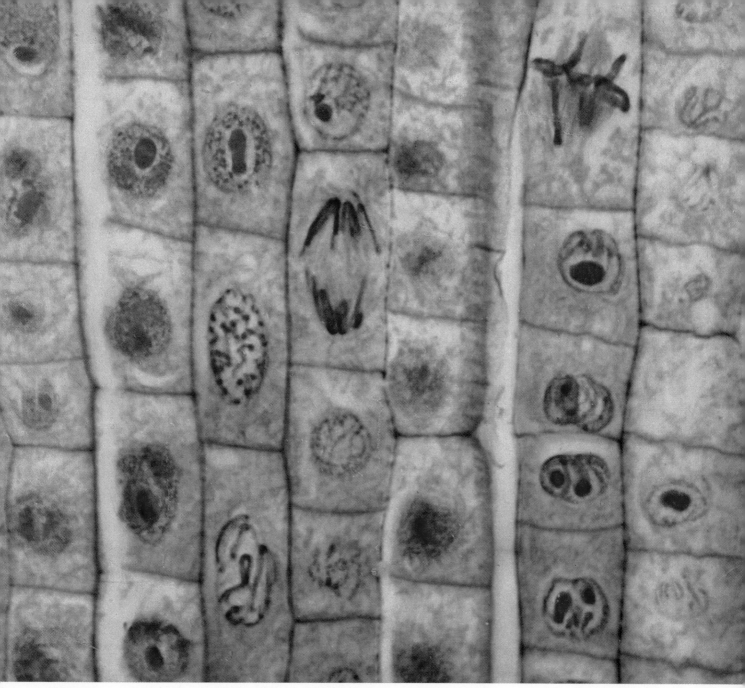

IN A STAINED, FILM-THIN SLICE OF A GROWING ONION ROOT, CELLS IN VARIOUS STAGES OF DIVISION ARE REVEALED BY THE MICROSCOPE

How Life Is Shaped

Cell division, the ceaseless production of units of living matter, is at the very heart of the evolutionary process. For when a cell splits so do its chromosomes, creating fresh supplies—and, through sex, new combinations—of genes. Dividing chromosomes can be seen clearly in the long cell at center above. How they can cause evolution through sex and chemistry is explained on the following pages.

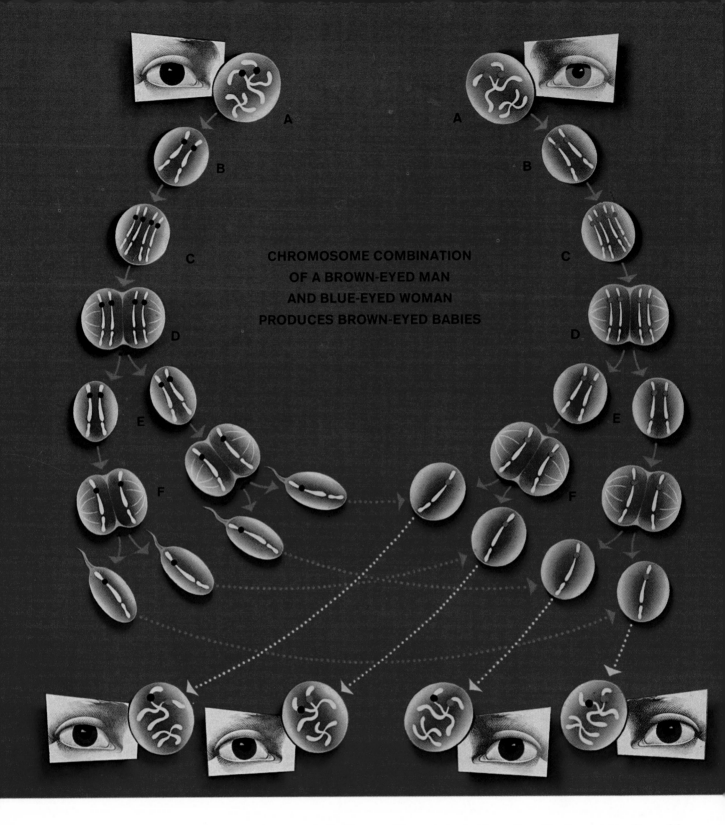

CHROMOSOME COMBINATION
OF A BROWN-EYED MAN
AND BLUE-EYED WOMAN
PRODUCES BROWN-EYED BABIES

In Generations of Cells
Nature's Laws of Inheritance

The mathematical laws of heredity discovered by Gregor Mendel, breeding peas in a quiet monastery garden, are difficult to apply to the lineage of a complex creature like man because most human characteristics are governed by more than one of the 40,000-odd genes in human chromosomes. For a few traits, however, like blue and brown eyes, the mathematics are not complicated by multiple causes and Mendel's laws hold true in their simplest form. If a purebred blue-eyed woman has children by a purebred brown-eyed man, all the babies will have their father's eyes. The cellular genetic steps which make this

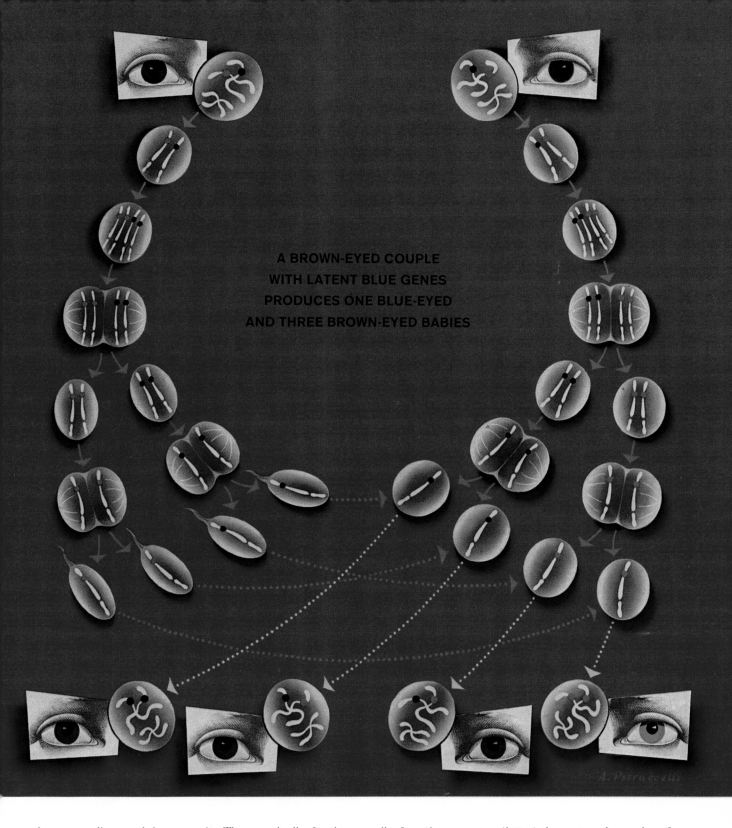

**A BROWN-EYED COUPLE
WITH LATENT BLUE GENES
PRODUCES ONE BLUE-EYED
AND THREE BROWN-EYED BABIES**

happen are diagramed above opposite. The normal cells of each parent are shown (A) with a token set of four chromosomes apiece. In producing eggs and sperms, the chromosomes tangled in each parent's cells pair up (B). Each chromosome duplicates itself (C). The cells divide once (D and E), then divide again (F), so that four new cells are produced, each one containing half as many chromosomes, and half as many genes, as the parent cell. This process is called reduction division, or meiosis, and the new cells that are formed are the eggs or sperms.

When sperms are united with eggs and fertilize them to make cells of growing youngsters (*bottom*), they restore the number of chromosomes to normal and give each child one blue-eyed gene (shown by a blue dot) and one brown-eyed gene (brown dot). The brown-eyed gene is dominant and it suppresses the effects of the blue-eyed one, giving all the children brown eyes. The children keep the recessive genes latent in their cells, and when they in turn reproduce with similar hybrids through the same sequence of cell divisions (*above*), they are likely to have two brown-eyed hybrids like themselves, one brown-eyed purebred like their father and one blue-eyed purebred like their mother.

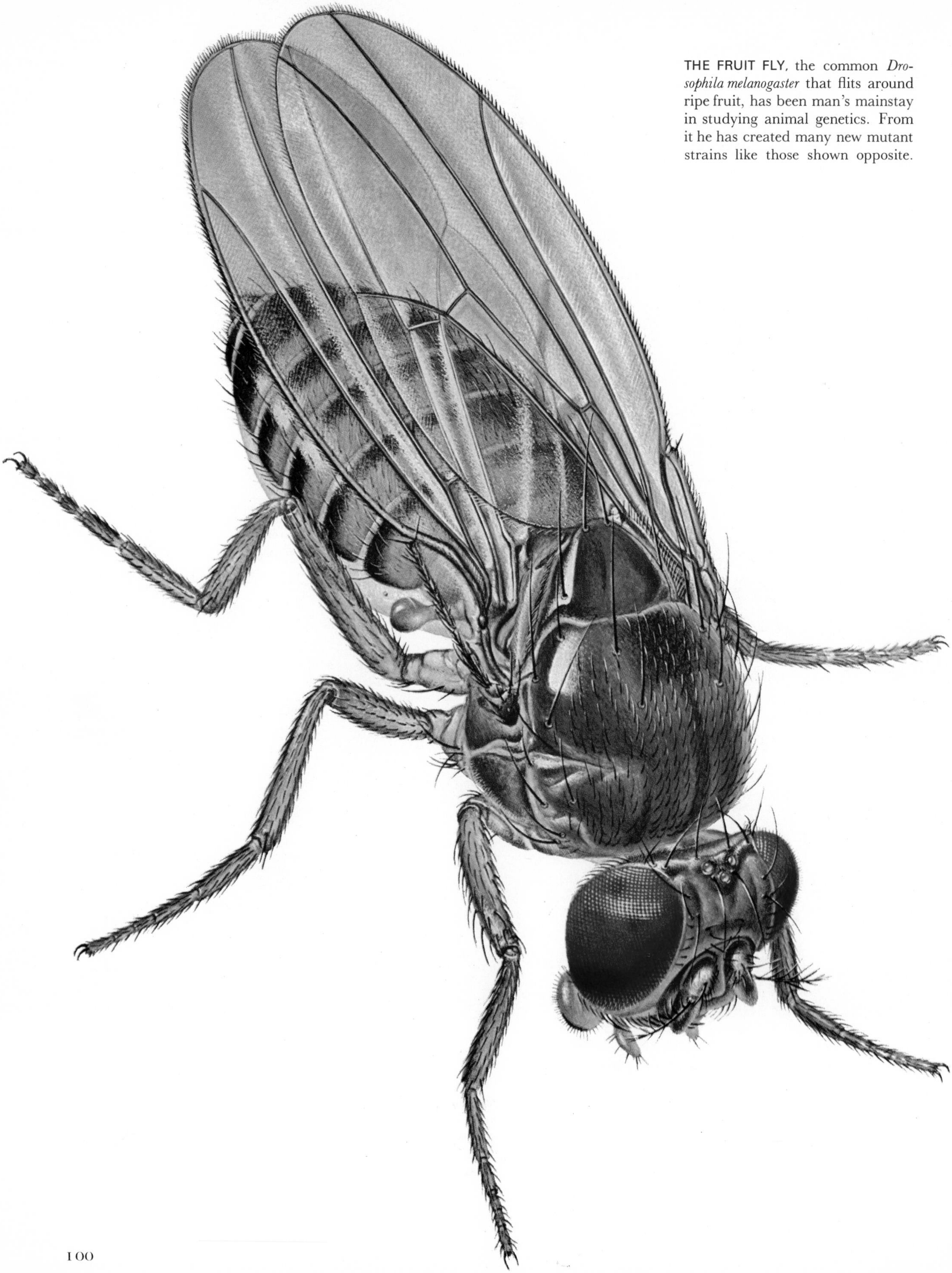

THE FRUIT FLY, the common *Drosophila melanogaster* that flits around ripe fruit, has been man's mainstay in studying animal genetics. From it he has created many new mutant strains like those shown opposite.

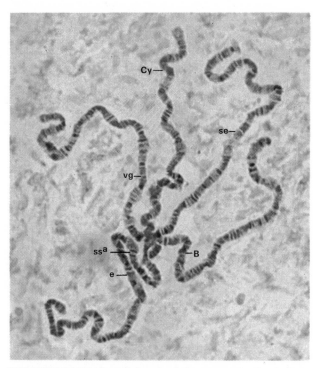

THE DARK BANDS in a fly's paired chromosomes show where its genes are. The genes have been carefully mapped to learn which gene controls which characteristic of the fly. Genes damaged at the points marked above produce the odd flies at right.

The Geneticists' Guinea Pig

What investigators cannot do with human beings, they can do with fruit flies. This wonderful insect, an eighth of an inch long, produces new generations profusely every 10 to 15 days, takes up little lab space and has a genetic make-up of four pairs of chromosomes. By normal breeding, biologists have brought to light an amazing amount of natural variability in its few chromosomes: changes in eye color, wing size and shape, abdomen markings and bristle arrangement. They have also observed new mutant traits springing up spontaneously and have even learned how to make mutations artificially through X rays. In short, they have demonstrated that fruit flies possess a wealth of genes for adapting themselves to the rigors of natural selection—and also a great ability to develop altered genes.

THE SIX MUTANT FLIES at right all derived spontaneously from the normal fly opposite. Aristapedia occurs when a fly's antenna becomes leglike, with claws and joints, although it is nonfunctional for walking. All of the other mutants are named self-descriptively except the wingless fly; it does have small vestigial wings.

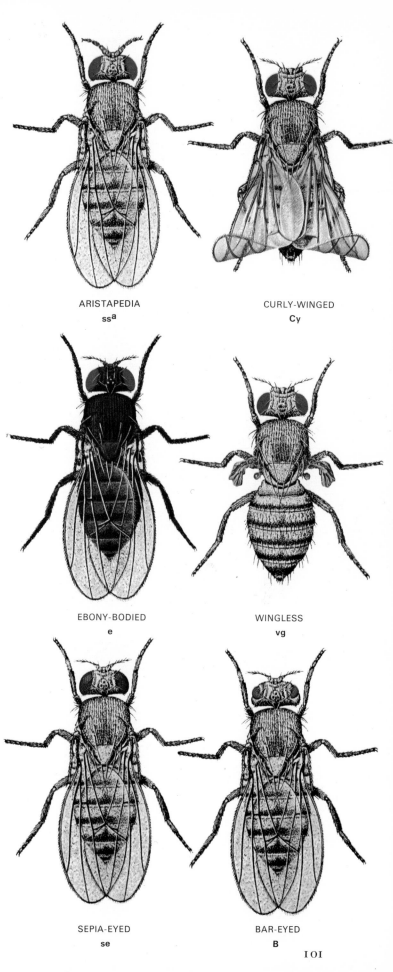

ARISTAPEDIA
ss^a

CURLY-WINGED
Cy

EBONY-BODIED
e

WINGLESS
vg

SEPIA-EYED
se

BAR-EYED
B

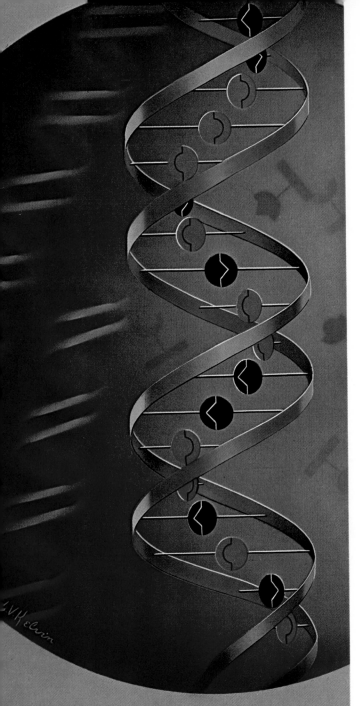

EVOLUTION'S KEY is DNA, a spiral molecule with two coils, linked by four interlocking chemical subunits (*below*). The sequence in which these are arranged determines heredity.

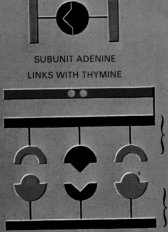

SUBUNIT ADENINE
LINKS WITH THYMINE

SUBUNIT GUANINE
LINKS WITH CYTOSINE

PROTEIN INGREDIENTS . . .

FETCHED BY TRANSFER RNA . . .

ASSEMBLED BY TEMPLATE RNA

1. How DNA acts to control body chemistry and growth by producing the right kinds of proteins is shown in these diagrams. First DNA unwinds (*above*) to expose a strip of subunits.

4. The DNA code is carried by RNA from the nucleus (*top*) to another body, a ribosome (*bottom*). This is a protein factory where RNA assembles the right chemicals to make the protein.

The Basic Chemistry of Life

In every chromosome in every cell of every individual is the chemical stuff that genes are made of—a miraculous molecule that makes a mouse a mouse or a man a man. It is called DNA. In its spiral structure (*diagram at left*), the arrangement of its four chemical subunits serves as a coded set of building

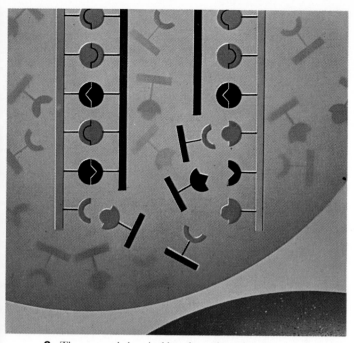

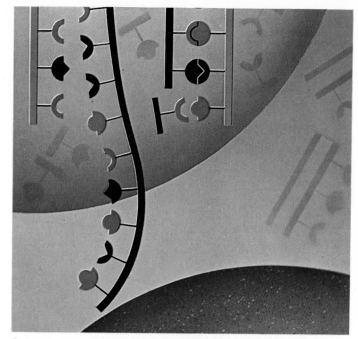

2. The exposed chemical bonds on the subunits attract matching chemical units from those drifting about loose in the nucleus, and assemble them into a molecule in the proper sequence.

3. The new molecule, which is called RNA, then leaves the nucleus, bearing in its pattern the "code" of DNA. Scientists do not know whether two RNA chains form (*above*) or only one.

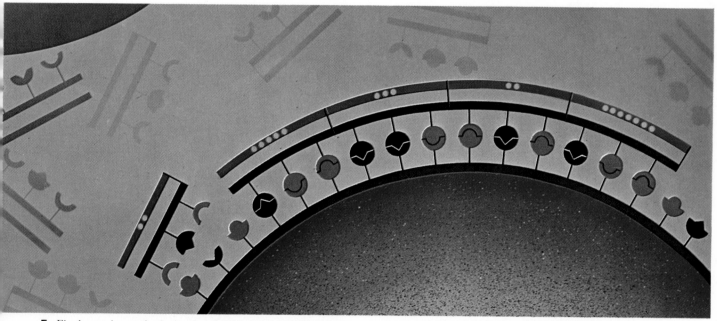

5. Final protein synthesis involves two types of RNA. One type, "transfer" RNA (*left*), moves about in the cell, impelled by electrical forces, and brings back raw materials for proteins to the ribosome. There the "template" RNA waits with its bonding points exposed, assembling bit by bit the incoming ingredients according to the pattern it originally got from DNA.

instructions for the whole organism. The number of possible sequences is larger than the number of subatomic particles in the universe, and theoretically permits an equal number of different individuals.

The way DNA directs growth and body chemistry is diagrammed above. Unwinding, it matches new chemical building blocks to its own sequence and thus creates other molecules called RNA. These in turn go out into the cell and by a similar process of matching create an array of special protein molecules which the cell uses as tools to build its own structure and to perform its function in the body.

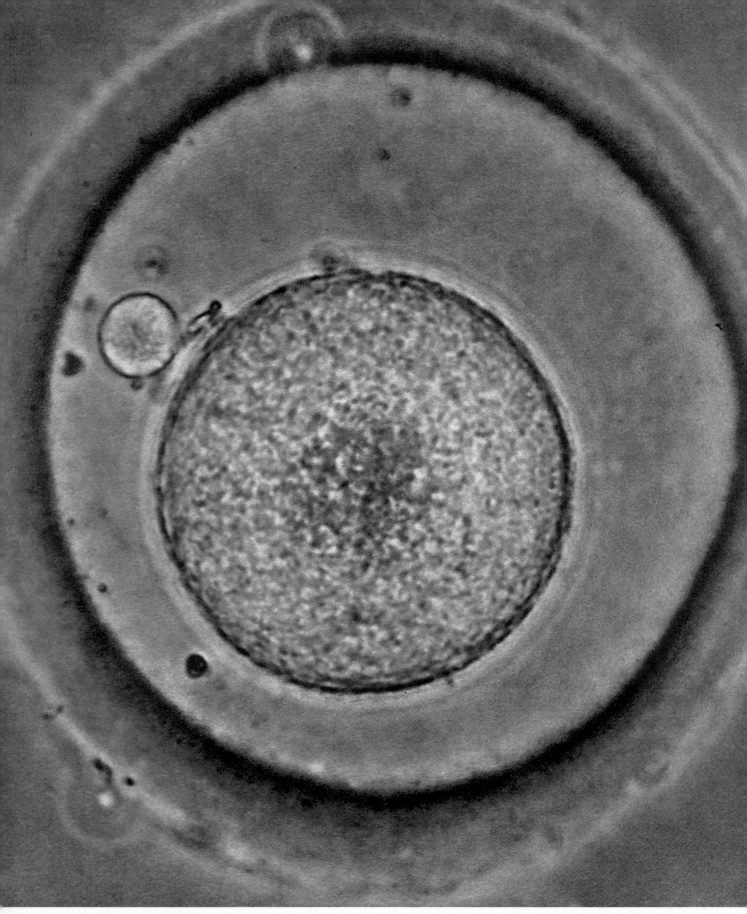

A HUMAN EGG, magnified 2,000 times, is a special giant cell produced in the ovaries of females. Its dark nucleus contains half as many chromosomes as normal body cells and is encircled by yellow cytoplasm stocked with growth enzymes. Outside the cytoplasm is a light-colored protective ring containing a "polar body" (left), a runt, nonproductive sister cell of the egg.

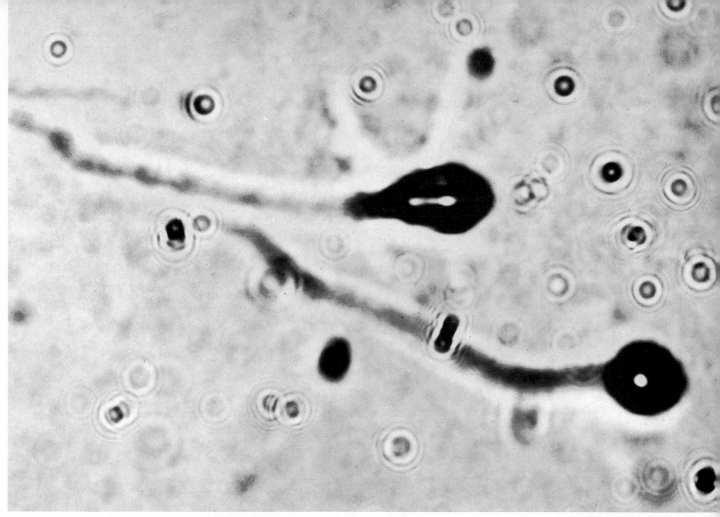

A HUMAN SPERM CELL, free-swimming and tadpole-shaped, is about 50,000 times less massive than a woman's egg but contains just as many child-deciding chemicals. Some of these sperms are "male"; they carry Y chromosomes which join with the exclusively X chromosomes of eggs to make XYs, or boys. Other sperms carry X chromosomes and make XXs, or girls.

New Combinations through Sex

If all life on earth were nothing but growth, simply a succession of splitting cells and self-replicating DNA, evolution would be very slow indeed. But fortunately a special kind of sexual cell division takes place in the reproductive organs of most plants and animals, called meiosis. It creates cells like the human egg and sperm, each with only half the genes and half the DNA of its parents. When egg and sperm are joined, a new individual with a full set of chromosomes is created—complete, but different from each parent.

Many plants and animals can reproduce asexually. A worm can be cut in half, and will grow into two identical individuals. Even a human egg can be split in two—a phenomenon which results in identical twins. But this asexual splitting merely increases the population of a species without increasing its diversity. Only by a constant mixing of genes is life given a choice of new kinds of individuals which can then be tested in the fires of evolution and survival.

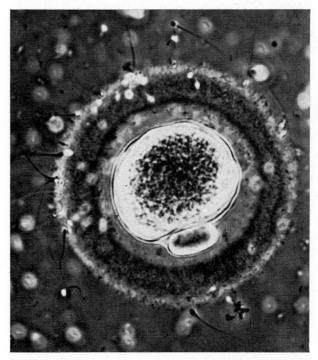

FERTILIZATION occurs as sperm cells pierce the envelope of an egg. The first sperm to reach the nucleus merges with it, bringing its complement of chromosomes up to normal cell number.

The Need for New Genes

Although sex constantly reshuffles the DNA deck of cards, it cannot create new genes. The best it can do is hit on various new combinations of old genes already in existence; these in time create improved types of highly specialized creatures which may survive and flourish for eons. The dinosaurs are a good example. But when climates change, making the environment hostile, groups of once well-adapted animals must either perish or come up with new genes that make possible new traits.

And in fact new genes do appear periodically as mutants. They are thought to stem from accidents which befall individual atoms in DNA synthesis. Man can induce them by poisoning a cell with powerful chemicals or treating its atoms to radiation. But the result of such crude methods is almost al-

NORMAL CHROMOSOMES DURING CELL DIVISION IN A TRILLIUM SEPARATE INTO TWO SETS AND WITHDRAW TO OPPOSITE ENDS OF THE CELL

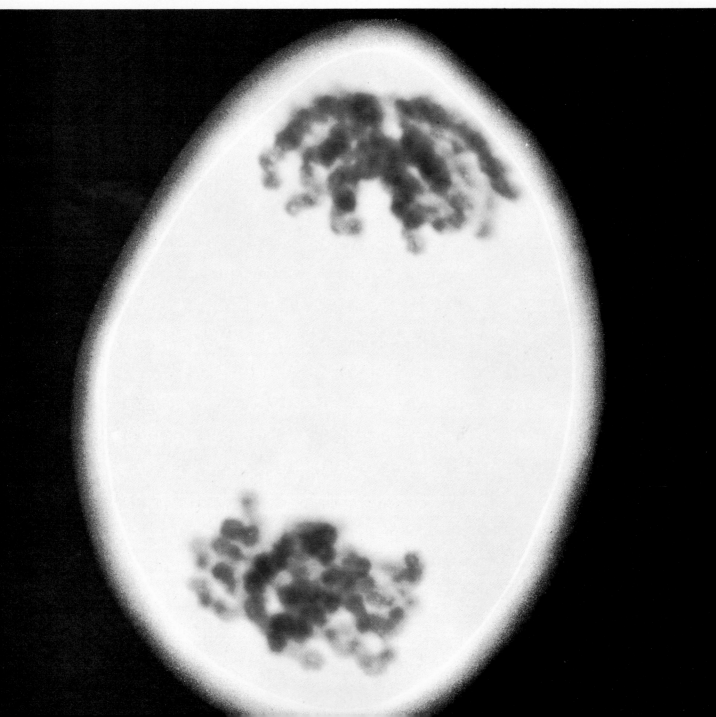

ways monstrous—a wingless fruit fly or a set of abnormal chromosomes like the ones below. This, of course, is the potential danger that atomic weapons hold for the human species. The mutations of nature may be equally drastic but more often have minor effects on the individual—a few atoms out of place through pure accident or the action of natural radiation from space. Though seldom fruitful, the mutations created in the laboratory have taught investigators one fact of enormous importance: most mutant genes are recessive. In other words, new genes are likely to lie low and increase in variety in a species until a change in the environment makes them useful. Then when most members of the species are hard-pressed or dying, a few pairs of double-recessive freaks could find themselves successful.

IN A MUTANT IRRADIATED CELL, CHROMOSOME SETS FAIL TO GO TO THE CELL'S ENDS AND ONE PAIR FAILS TO SEPARATE, FORMING A BRIDGE

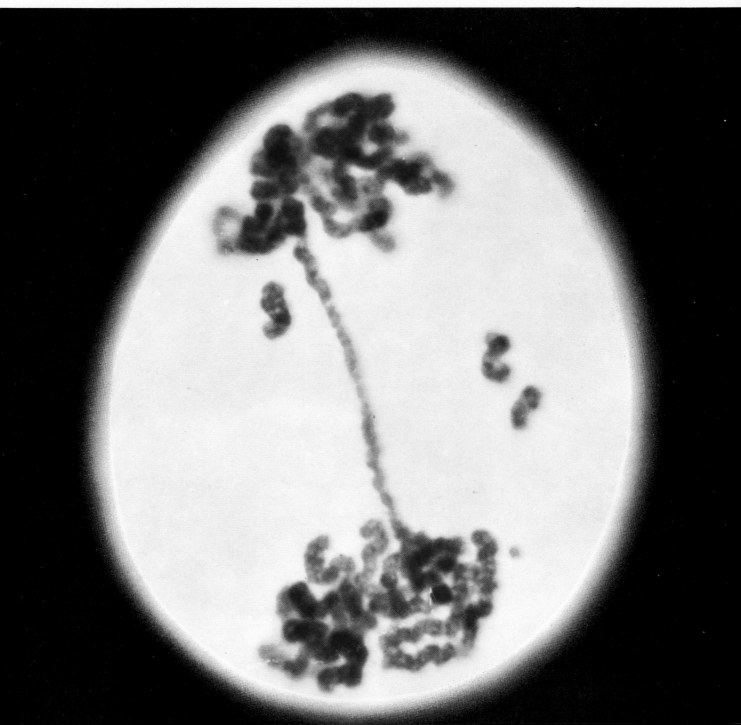

5

A Half Billion Years of Creation

Long before Darwin scaled the high sea cliff in the Cape Verdes and found sea shells buried in its limestone face, men had been digging shells, petrified wood and other ancient objects from the earth. Some of these curios strangely resembled the bones of animals. Though a few authorities held that they had been molded into familiar forms by Satan to deceive mankind, the general notion was that fossils had been formed by natural forces in chance imitation of life. They were "stone cast in animal molds."

The Reverend John Ray, a 17th Century Cambridge University lecturer, was enough of a naturalist to recognize that some of the shells he collected in the mountains were exactly like other shells he gathered on the seashore. Others were obviously the remains of fish that lived only in the ocean deeps. To account for marine fossils in the mountains, Ray resorted to ingenious interpretations of Old Testament earth history. He concluded after much study that the fossils were washed up to their places of deposit when the Bible's 40 days and 40 nights of unceasing deluge filled the reservoirs of the world and caused the "Fountains of the Great Deep" to break forth. In the tremendous surge that overflowed the globe, he reasoned, the fish and other creatures of the sea were simply swept up rivers and carried through underground streams, right into the high mountains.

The flood theory of fossils was finally destroyed by the dawning recognition that the face of the earth, with its mountains and valleys and plains, was slowly shaped by continuing natural forces—the "uniformitarianism" of geologist Charles Lyell. But it took some doing, by the infant sciences of geology and archeology, to give this evolutionary concept enough time to operate in—a few thousands of millions of years instead of a few thousand years. Not until the start of the 19th Century did the French scholar Lamarck make a convincing case for the theory that fossils were not chance concretions or devilish ones, but the natural remains of once-living plants and animals.

Paris nevertheless became quite excited when Lamarck's more illustrious colleague, Georges Cuvier, professor of natural history at the Collège de France, announced in 1796 the discovery of elephant bones in the soil of the Paris area itself. Soon the amazing Cuvier and other diggers were unearthing even stranger denizens of an unknown and unsuspected past—reptiles big as whales, mammoths with long tusks and heavy coats of hair, bears, wolves and other creatures that bore only a superficial similarity to living species. From a few of their bones Cuvier, sorcererlike, put the animals back together with such startling realism that Balzac marveled: "Is Cuvier not the greatest poet of our century? Our immortal naturalist has reconstructed worlds from blanched bones. He picks up a piece of gypsum and says to us 'See!' Suddenly stone turns into animals and another world unrolls before our eyes."

Like the living members of the animal kingdom, such collections of ancient animals did not come in a random assortment but could be classified into species and genera. Cuvier counted 90 species, and some whole genera, that had utterly disappeared from the earth. What could have brought about such terrible decimation, he wondered, and how could the lost species have been succeeded by still others before the animals of "the present creation" appeared?

To find the answers to such riddles, Cuvier set out to learn how the fossil creatures had been entombed, and to find out all he could about the earth of their distant time. He enlisted the aid of Alexandre Brongniart, a professor of mineralogy and head of the famous Sèvres china factory. For years the two studied the Paris countryside in depth. They discovered that layer was piled upon layer: one stony bed filled with millions of sea shells, and just below it a different formation with a scattering of land shells. Other strata were studded with the bones of extinct giant mammals. Still others had no fossils at all.

Cuvier and Brongniart tried to interpret the puzzling succession of vanished worlds. At times, as they explained to rapt Parisian audiences, the seas had flooded into the Paris basin. At other times the salt waters had receded, and the dry land had been dotted with fresh-water lakes. Again the seas had returned, and again they had rolled back. In deposits laid down during the sea eras were the shells and bones of ocean life; in sediments marking the bottoms of the fresh-water lakes lay fresh-water shells and the bones of land animals. There was no mixing of the land and sea deposits; one ended and the other began.

All of this, which seems so obvious now, was brand-new at the time, a new interpretation of earth history and a new key to past and present. At about the same time, an English surveyor named William Smith was making similar observations in his own country and coming to similar conclusions. "Each stratum contains organized fossils peculiar to itself," he reported. In 1815 Smith published a painstaking geologic map of England, showing the strata that underlay

**SOME OLD IDEAS
THAT WENT ASTRAY**

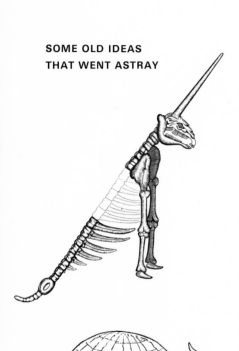

Early naturalists, lacking a firm knowledge of anatomy and evolution, often reconstructed fossils to look like animals they knew (the turtle) or imagined (the unicorn). These reconstructions were made from the bones of the extinct mammoth.

the landscape and proving again that "the same species of fossils are found in the same stratum, even at wide distances."

The implications of these studies were extremely disturbing to the men making them. Cuvier was a scientist intensely devoted to the truth, but even with the succession of species before him he could not admit that one species had arisen from another. To have done so, embracing the evolutionary ideas of Lamarck, would have denied his strong Huguenot faith in a special creation. Cuvier preferred another explanation, a series of vast cataclysms wiping out the old and clearing the stage for new creations.

D ARWIN, confronted by the same relationship of fossil species to living ones, saw that the latter were the modified descendants of the former. Carrying the case to its full conclusion in *The Origin of Species* and in *The Descent of Man*, he was forced to assume an unbroken chain of organisms intermediate between the first forms of life and man. Here was a theory hopefully subject to proof; where was the proof? Where were the bones of this multitude of organisms? Surely many of them should have survived in the earth. Yet the fossils found up to Darwin's day, including those unearthed by Cuvier, Brongniart and Smith, supplied only the most fragmentary evidence. Where were the missing links?

The search went on in Europe, in the Americas, in Java, in China, in Africa. By the middle of the 20th Century, a hundred years after publication of *The Origin*, the fossil record still was far from complete, and it could never be complete. On the other hand, it was filled in well enough so that scientists could undertake to trace the evolution of life in terms of its fossilized remains. The test of actuality could be applied. Had life evolved as the theory of evolution held?

So well buttressed was the record that an even more severe test could be brought to bear. Would the remains in the rocks show the spread of new gene frequencies, as the modern biological theory of evolution required? Could evolutionary change be tracked through successive populations of various species? There was some doubt that so complex a task—amounting to a fusion of paleontology and genetics—could successfully be achieved. Nevertheless a number of scientists undertook the work, particularly George Gaylord Simpson, E. H. Colbert, Theodosius Dobzhansky, A. S. Romer and Ernst Mayr. Studying the actual fossils, their anatomy, their relationships and their times, such men put together the complex story of the rise and development of life on earth.

The story is well documented through all but its opening chapters. Our planet and the rest of the solar system are now reckoned to be about 4.5 billion years of age, and for most of that incomprehensibly long time the earth was lifeless. In the very oldest exposed rocks of the various continental cores, or shields, which have been dated as far back as 3.6 billion years, there is no trace of fossils, and for good reason. If life began as a molecule with the miraculous capacity to reproduce itself, developing later as a single cell and then into a cluster of a few soft cells, it could not possibly leave even the shadowiest imprint behind. Yet somewhere on earth, somehow life indeed began, possibly more than two billion years ago. It was already old by the time its first traces—single-celled microorganisms, identifiable neither as plants nor as animals—were left in the rocks.

The earliest animal fossils so far found are those of primitive water-dwelling invertebrates, animals without backbones. Already they were, as Dobzhansky noted, "quite elaborate and advanced in body structure." Some had jointed bodies and shells. They were in fact creatures well adapted to their environment, the ancient, silent seas. Then, in rocks formed about 425 million years

SOME OLD SHELLS THAT LED MAN ASTRAY

"Serpent stones" were thought to be remains of snakes and dragons by early naturalists. They are actually very common invertebrate shell fossils. The creatures, with diameters from a half inch to over six feet, died out some 60 million years ago.

ago, the remains of a new kind of creature appear. Named an ostracoderm and looking like a crudely formed fish, it had an internal skeleton in contrast to the absence of any such structure in the invertebrates, and it was armored with bony scales. For all its firm build, the ostracoderm, an ancestor of the modern lamprey, was jawless. It made its way along the bottom, sucking up food.

As time went on, the rock record shows that this limited creature began to lose out to something still newer in the world, a fish with jaws. Such a fish no longer had to confine itself to scavenging along the bottom; it could eat many kinds of food—or even seize prey—at any level. Some of the jawless fish, it appears, were born with a slightly altered gill arch shaped like a V turned sideways. With only a few related changes the V made an effective jaw.

The bony jaw, like any favorable change, spread throughout the fish population. Because a fish with well-furnished jaws could capture more food, it was more likely to survive and leave offspring. In addition, its spread into new waters opened many new opportunities. Even so, these early jawed fishes, the placoderms and acanthodians, were themselves replaced by different and overwhelmingly successful descendants. Mutation and selection produced better fins for better swimming. The new fishes whose remains began to appear in the ancient-sea sediments had tail fins, which could drive their possessors forward with a gentle back-and-forth sculling motion. They also had dorsal and anal fins to serve as stabilizers and keels, and paired pectoral and pelvic fins for controlling movement. Fishes so equipped went on to occupy all of the earth's waters and in the end, though not immediately, to outnumber all other vertebrates combined. One part of the earth, the biggest, was pre-empted.

But a fish that differed significantly from all its forebears appeared in the rocks laid down about 390 million years ago. The front of its skull could be raised and lowered a bit, a change that would ease the shock when the jaws snapped shut. Its teeth were sharply pointed and well adapted to grasping prey. A single bone articulated the fins with the structural girdle. Such a single bone and related structures were to become familiar in later ages as the leg bones of land-dwelling animals. These unusual fish, called crossopterygians (lobe-fins), had made an even more vital change. In addition to gills, they were developing lungs. "The crossopterygians are to us perhaps the most important of fishes," said Colbert, "they were our far distant but direct forebears."

Some 365 million years ago, some of these crossopterygians ventured out on the land. It is a plausible guess that they lived in streams which dried in the

The development of the modern horse has been traced back some 60 million years from the tall, graceful animal of today to a short-necked creature not much larger than a domestic cat. Originally the horse was a forest dweller with many toes, well adapted to travel on the soft, moist earth of tropical North America. As the climate grew colder and the forest thinned into an open grassy plain, the horse slowly developed hard single toes for traveling on dry land, and complicated grinding teeth for feeding on the scanty herbage of the Great Plateau.

EOHIPPUS
Eocene—58 million years ago

MESOHIPPUS
Oligocene—36 million years ago

MERYCHIPPUS
Miocene—25 million years ago

drought of summer into a few scattered pools. Did the fish struggle and flop from one drying pool to another with more water? No one knows, but those fish that were able to stay out of the water for a longer time certainly would have been the survivors and would have left behind progeny with their own greater ability to breathe in the air.

In eastern Greenland fossil hunters have found a creature more advanced than the most advanced crossopterygians; it was one of the primitive amphibians. The *Ichthyostega* combined a fish tail with lungs and well-developed legs and feet. With their lungs and "walking legs," these early fish-out-of-water had a whole new source of food open to them. They could crawl along the banks of streams and snap up the insects which were beginning to swarm there. And the earth lay open before them—for no other vertebrates were there to contest it.

Not that life was easy for the first amphibians. They had gravity to contend with—several times greater a factor on dry land than in the buoying water—and desiccation, the drying-out action of the air, as well. Nevertheless they flourished. During the next 50 million to 100 million years, they spread far and evolved into many different species. Their fossilized bones and imprints are found in Europe, in North America and in certain parts of Asia.

These newcomers to the land, however, never succeeded in wholly freeing themselves from the water. Although they learned to rely fully on their lungs, and to amble along the swampy riverbanks on sturdy legs derived from the ancestral fins, they always returned to the water to lay their soft, jelly-coated eggs. Reproduction tied them to the past, and to the water.

In the fullness of time, mutation and selection again performed their wonders. Some of the amphibians developed an egg which was encased in a firm, leathery shell and thus was far better protected than the soft eggs of the fish and the other amphibians. This new and better egg was internally fertilized and deposited in some safe place until the young were hatched. With its perfection, the egg-laying animals won their full freedom from the water. A well-protected embryo could develop in its own private pool, the amniotic cavity of the egg, guarded not only from dryness but also from the hazards of the land world outside. The new and freer group which was evolving in this way, from amphibian ancestry, was the reptiles.

The oldest fossil eggs ever found come from sediments in Texas dated at about 280 million years ago. When the eggs were laid the reptiles were already

PLIOHIPPUS

Pliocene—13 million years ago

EQUUS

Pleistocene and recent—1 million years ago

ANATOMICAL SIMILARITIES
AMONG DIFFERENT SPECIES

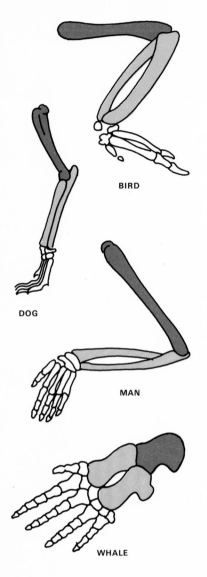

BIRD

DOG

MAN

WHALE

An anatomical comparison of the "arm" of a whale, a dog, a bird and man shows that while proportions differ, the structural plan is identical. When Darwin noted this "similar framework of bones" among amphibians, reptiles, birds and mammals, he concluded descent must progress "with slow and slight successive modifications."

well advanced. In the absence of earlier eggs, it is hard for scientists to tell exactly when the amphibians crossed the threshold into reptiledom, for the earliest known reptiles are so amphibianlike that their assignment to one category or the other is largely a matter of opinion. In this area of life, however, there was no missing link; all the gradations from amphibian to reptile exist with a clarity seldom equaled in paleontology.

With their new-found freedom from the water, the reptiles literally took over the earth, and the "age of reptiles" began. For the first time the land was widely occupied by vertebrate life. As time went on and natural selection arrived at variations to fit all the diverse environments the earth afforded, the reptiles —as their predecessors had done and as their descendants would do—split, or radiated, into a great many groups with different structures and different ways of life. Some of the reptiles returned to the water whence their ancestors had come, though they never went back to the ancestral structures. Those which returned continued to breathe with their lungs, while their reptilian legs became modified into paddles or fins. Some of these marine reptiles looked strikingly like the modern whales and porpoises.

STILL other reptiles ventured into the air, which was unoccupied except by the insects, buzzing about close to the ground. With wings formed by a fold of skin, functioning like those of the modern bat, the reptiles hunted from the air, swooping down after fish near the surfaces of lakes and lagoons. They were skilled gliders, easily manipulating their elongated heads to seek or seize prey; some used their long tails with flapping ends for balance.

For all their airworthiness, these reptiles did not give rise to the birds. The fossil record proves that the birds arose independently, from the same ancestors —the archosaurs—which produced the flying reptiles. Two of the earliest birds fell into a coral lagoon in what is now Bavaria, in Germany. As the fine lime ooze settled around them, they were preserved in remarkable detail. The long head with its sharp teeth, the long neck, the strong hind legs and the rich, herringbone pattern of feathers all are molded in the most exquisite detail on the fine lithographic limestone. If the long flight feathers and the unique row of feathers down either side of the tail had not been imprinted in stone, few would concede that so reptilian a creature could have been so clothed. But the feathers were true bird feathers, and *Archaeopteryx* is classified as a bird, the earliest and most primitive of the group that in time would take over the province of the air.

Even before this, when the reptiles were in their first heyday, one of their small, obscure groups began to change. Some of the animals skulking through the lush vegetation of the great swamps of the time had longer and slimmer leg bones than those of other reptiles. Their improved ability to get around counted heavily in natural selection. These were the synapsids, whose destiny was to form an evolutionary bridge between the reptiles and what would become the mammals. Reptilian life was proliferating in all directions at the time and synapsids, like other subclasses, came in a variety of shapes and sizes—everything from wolf-sized creatures to brutes of half a ton or more. One order among them, the therapsids, had a curious mixture of reptilian and mammalian characteristics. As disclosed in specimens that the fossil hunter Dr. Robert Broom dug up as early as 1897 in the Karroo deposits of South Africa, the therapsid had a secondary palate, a most nonreptilian structure, enabling it to breathe while eating. Instead of the simple peg teeth of the reptiles, it had sharply contrasted incisors, canines and cheek teeth—for masticating food instead of bolting it whole. Its legs were drawn underneath the body, which was thus hoisted a useful height above the ground. This new, higher-slung animal was much faster when the need arose than the typical reptile with ungainly legs and a body that tended to drag along the ground.

Among the descendants of the synapsids were some small animals with uniform body temperatures; like the birds they were warm-blooded. An insulating coat of hair helped to protect them from the heat as well as the cold. Perhaps at first there were very few of them, for not many of their bones have been found. The few fragments retrieved do not show positively how they produced their young. Dr. Colbert, however, believes that although they may have been egg-layers like their reptilian ancestors, they also suckled their young, in something of the manner of the anachronistic modern monotremes, the platypus, or duckbill, of Australia and the spiny anteater of New Guinea.

The suckling of the young by a few scattered animals—if anyone had been present to appraise it—might have seemed of no moment. From the standpoint of selection, it was indeed all-important, and one of the determinative changes of all evolutionary time. The fish and reptiles laid large numbers of eggs, but relatively few of them ever hatched. Of those that did, not many of the untended young survived. The individual counted for little. The small animals nursing their young suddenly made the survival of offspring no longer a matter of chance, but of constitutional and genotypic fitness to survive.

The new mammals, for that is what they were, had only a few offspring, but the food supply of these few was assured and they were protected as no other creatures' young had been. Thus the few, in the end, could outnumber and outlast the many. At about the same time, perhaps 100 million years ago, selection developed another great improvement—the placenta, an arrangement of blood vessels through which an embryo could be supplied with food and oxygen while developing inside the mother's body. The ultimate protection had been found at last, and it was protection at the stage that mattered most. It directly affected survival and the continuance of the kind. By this advance the mammals' future was set.

B^UT they did not race into that future. Even an advantageous pattern must have time and the opportunity to spread. Not until the reptiles began to decline did the mammals branch out phenomenally. Then they began to move into every part of the earth. During the next 27 million years, the long dawn of our own contemporary geologic era, the radiation of the mammals was as "explosive" as that of the reptiles had been. From the first furtive little mammals came every mammalian order now existing—and many that have become extinct.

Among this great array so rapidly spreading over the earth were the tree shrews and some of their relatives. They were of vast importance as the apparent founders of the primate family, whose branches led to the monkeys, the apes and man. Not much larger than squirrels and superficially resembling them, the tree shrews had slightly bigger brains than those of their molelike ancestors. Their fingers and toes had a greater range of movement, which helped as they climbed high in the trees in search of insects and fruit.

Some of their relatives developed a hand that could close quickly and surely around a branch, and slender legs that let them hop nimbly through the trees. These were the lemurs, which once lived in many parts of the world but flourish today mainly on the island of Madagascar. The lorises, now living in India, Southeast Asia and Africa, developed somewhat forward-turned eyes, a place-

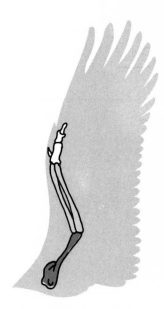

Although the wings of birds (above) and mammals (below) are based on the same anatomical plan, they are quite different in detail. The "finger" bones of the bird are fused and the wing's support is provided by a greatly lengthened arm bone.

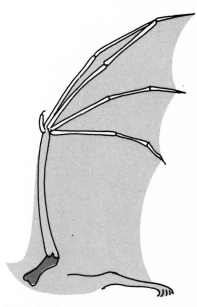

The bat's wing is supported by four long "finger" bones, with the "thumb" projecting through the wing to end in a claw for hanging from branches or caves. The wing is actually just a fold of skin attached to the body and to the hind legs.

ment common to all the higher primates. Another relative was the tarsier, which had a more efficient grasp and was generally adapted for life in the trees. The structure of its surprised, gnomelike face and lips, and of its brain, led a number of authorities to classify the kitten-sized animal as a connecting link between the early prosimians and the modern anthropoids. More explicit links are still missing. Several fossils which were thought at first to be those of transitional primates have since been discredited. The trouble is that the early primates dwelt in dank tropical forests, where their remains were most unlikely to be long preserved. By about 25 million years ago, however, the transitions had been accomplished; monkeys lived in the New World and monkeys, along with a variety of apelike animals, in the Old World.

The green world of the treetops into which the primates had moved was a safe but restricted one. A strong sense of smell and acute hearing were not as essential as on the ground, but the primates with freer hands, better eyes and stereoscopic vision were the ones to survive such predators as snakes and such hazards as falling to the ground—and to leave descendants. Gradually the primate brain changed from a primitive "smell" organ to a more advanced "sight" brain. Along with enlargement of the brain came a rounding out of the head and, in some of the African primates, enlargement of the whole body. This forced some groups to develop a different mode of locomotion. Too heavy to run through the branches, holding fast with hands and feet, they took to swinging along with a new motion of the arm, or brachiation. This activity favored anatomical changes in the wrist, elbow, shoulder and thoracic region; all these took on the form that is common today to apes and men.

One of the first of the incipient brachiators was Proconsul. Mary and Louis Leakey, the fossil hunters, found his skull at Lake Victoria in Africa in 1948. Proconsul stood just below the parting of the ways between ape and human stems. Some of his descendants became highly specialized: they went on to become the great apes of today, the gorilla, the orangutan, the gibbon and the chimpanzee. A few took another course. In time they adopted a more varied diet and increasingly came down from the trees to forage on the ground. Slowly they changed along a line quite different from that of the other apes—a line that man, from his perspective, can see as leading up to himself.

THIS whole, necessarily abbreviated outline of life's development also has been drawn from man's perspective. From that point of view all the major links, except the still-only-presumed one from invertebrates to fish, now exist in unchallengeable bone and stone: the links from fish to amphibians, from amphibians to reptiles, from reptiles to mammals, from an ambiguous little mammal to the primates, from the primitive primates to the apes, and finally to an early ape moving toward a new, upright way of life.

Innumerable other species arose, found their niches and continued. Others won temporary success but were replaced by different, more successful offspring, or succumbed to changes in environment. There was never a simple, clear-cut progression like a flight of steps. As Darwin pointed out, the growth of life was like that of a tree. But with the filling-in of the fossil record, life's growth could be followed throughout the latest half billion years of the earth's existence. The theory of evolution was substantiated and proved by the undisputable remains of the animals that lived and died during this long climb from the first organized forms to the immediate predecessors of man. Only the capping evidence of man's own emergence remained to be found.

A CANDIDATE FOR FOSSILIZATION, A SQUIRREL JOINS OTHER ANIMALS TRAPPED IN PAST MILLENNIA BY CALIFORNIA'S LA BREA TAR PITS

Fragments from the Past

Of the myriads of animal species that have lived on earth, concrete remains of only one in a thousand have been found in fossil form—teeth, shells, bones, tracks, eggs, imprints or even entire mummies. These clues to bygone life have been preserved in stone, coal, amber, ice and tar (above). A few of the most remarkable are shown on the following pages, either as fossils or in reconstructions.

STONY SEA LILIES of the extinct *Uintacrinus socialis* species were preserved in the crust of Kansas in Cretaceous times 90 million years ago. At that period a shallow ocean covered the plains, and these animals, related to today's starfishes and sea lilies, drifted about the surface in clusters, stroking food into their bodies along thread-lined grooves in their long, sinuous arms.

A FIERCE FISH, *Ichthyodectes* of the Cretaceous, was an early six-foot predator of the modern teleost group, akin to the salmon, herring and trout, with a completely hard, bony skeleton.

A FRAGILE DRAGONFLY, *Protolindenia wittei*, left a rare impress of its soft body as well as its harder, two-inch wings. During the Jurassic, some 150 million years ago, it flitted over Bavaria.

LEATHERY GLIDER, *Pterodactylus elegans*, also flew in Jurassic times. It had hollow bones and wings of skin but it lacked the feathers of the true birds which evolved at about the same time.

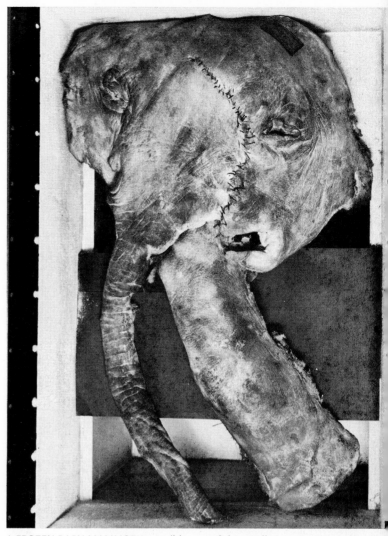

A FROZEN BABY MAMMOTH, possibly one of the woolly mammoths which roamed the tundra 22,000 years ago, was freed from the Arctic muck by the pressure hoses of Alaskan miners.

Animals in the Rocks

In the fossils laid down one after another and preserved by being petrified, dried out or pressed between and below successive layers of sediment in the earth's crust, man reads a clear, though fragmentary, history of emerging animal life on his planet. Among the earliest to leave traces of themselves were invertebrate sea creatures like jellyfishes or the plated, starfishlike sea lilies opposite. Much later came vertebrate fishes; then land-dwelling insects like dragonflies; then air-breathing vertebrates like pterodactyls; and last, the warm-blooded, big-brained mammals—like mice, men and mammoths —that nursed their young and could pass along techniques of living from generation to generation.

DINOSAUR TRACKS in Texas show where a huge plant eater of the brontosaur type waded over a hundred million years ago and was shadowed (three-toed tracks, *left*) by a smaller meat eater.

Relics of Giants

The most dramatic of all fossils are dinosaurs'. Prior to the 19th Century, when men dug up huge bones they were likely to think—with full justification—that they had stumbled onto buried titans. Now that geologists recognize the bones as remnants of monstrous reptiles, they can find other dinosaur traces as well—such as footprints (*left*) or eggs (*below*)—and they can distinguish all sizes of dinosaurs, from the colossi big enough to peer over rooftops down to speedy little fellows a foot or so long.

After reptiles first appeared—first evolved as vertebrates able to lay their eggs on dry land—they went on to split into many groups. One fathered present-day turtles. Another gave rise to mammals. Still another sired modern snakes and lizards. But the most conspicuous and varied group, the diapsid archosaurs, branched into crocodiles, flying reptiles, birds and—largest but not longest-lived—dinosaurs, some of which are shown on the following pages.

PROTOCERATOPS EGGS, about eight inches long, were laid in Mongolia during the Cretaceous by a smallish, six-foot dinosaur of the ornithischian order. Now brown and petrified, they were probably white when fresh. Their arrangement indicates that they were buried like sea-turtle eggs in a warm hollow of sand and then abandoned by their mother in typical reptile fashion.

A CAMARASAURUS BACKBONE is brought into relief from sandstone at Utah's Dinosaur National Monument by expert James Adams, working carefully with hammer, chisel, goggles and fine brush which he has at hand. Although smaller than most of its type, *Camarasaurus* was still more than 25 feet long —a wearisome rut to cut inch by inch with small hand tools.

The Diversified Dynasties of Dinosaurs

The first dinosaurs were comparatively small creatures running about on long hind legs and using their short forelimbs for grasping and tearing. As they multiplied they evolved into two main groups, distinguished by different pelvic-bone structure. One group, called the ornithischians, had pelves in which the lower bones were long and parallel. Most dinosaurs in this group ate plants and went on all fours. Some of them, like *Stegosaurus (opposite)* and *Styracosaurus (below)*, developed bizarre defenses of horns and plates. This armor was occasionally so ornate that it may well have deterred attackers by its look of utter unpalatability. But some of it, like the horns of *Triceratops (below, opposite)*, must have been lethal, especially when backed by several tons of charging flesh.

The other group, known as the saurischians and pictured on the following pages, had its lower pelvic bones angled and cemented in a strong arch that could support a two-legged way of life. Many of them did indeed go on two legs and, like *Tyrannosaurus*, were huge, swift, aggressive meat eaters. But some were plant eaters. They were so enormously heavy that they had to trudge on all fours despite their arched pelvic shape. The closest of all living relatives of the dinosaurs is the modern crocodile.

STYRACOSAURUS, though it looks like a rhinoceros from a big-game hunter's nightmare, was actually much larger than a rhinoceros and fully reptilian—a heavy-headed, huge-horned dinosaur 16 feet long and four tons in weight. Evolving some 80 million years ago in the late Cretaceous, it came at the end of the dinosaurs' reign, just before they all mysteriously perished.

STEGOSAURUS, an ornithischian of the Jurassic, was the American representative of a plate-backed race found around the world. Though impractical-looking, its general type persisted for many millions of years. But it still was the first large category of dinosaurs to become extinct.

TRICERATOPS, a ruffed, tricorn relative of *Styracosaurus* on the opposite page, roamed buffalolike in huge herds on the uplands of ancient Wyoming, Montana and Colorado. Although it was a peaceable plant eater, it probably could charge like a tank when aroused, and its three-pronged ram must have made it dangerous quarry for even the most terrible of the predatory dinosaurs.

THE SWAMP MONSTER *Brachiosaurus*, a saurischian of the late Jurassic, became the largest land animal of all time and also the largest of any kind except for modern whales. Up to 80 feet long and 40 feet high, it had developed so far from the two-legged gait of its ancestors that its forelimbs were longer than its hind ones and its back sloped up to its neck giraffe-fashion.

This and the fact that its nostrils opened out in a bulge at the top of its periscopic head indicate that it was most likely a deep wader, capable of fording large rivers. Conceivably it never came out on dry land at all because it needed water to buoy up the burden of its body. But the depth of footprints left by almost equally bulky brontosaurs suggests that it sometimes ventured at least into shallow water, floating its long tail behind it. Impressive though it looked, *Brachiosaurus* was a stupid, sleepy beast with a slow rate of metabolism—and got along with less brain per pound of flesh than any other vertebrate that has ever lived.

125

THE AWFUL ONSLAUGHT of *Tyrannosaurus rex*, a mighty saurischian meat eater of the Cretaceous, 50 feet long and 18 feet high, closes in on two semiaquatic ornithischian duck-billed dinosaurs caught off guard, away from deep water to which they would ordinarily escape. Although more than 30 feet long themselves, the duckbills were no match for *Tyrannosaurus'* tremendous jaws and dagger-sharp, six-inch teeth. Their own teeth numbered 2,000 but were flat grinders packed together like a pavement and adapted for munching fresh-water plants which they grubbed in the sluggish rivers of the flat Cretacean landscape. In the distance at left run three saurischian "ostrich dinosaurs"—a trim, fleet-footed group which probably ate anything, including stolen eggs from the nests of their cumbersome kin.

6

The Search for Mankind's Ancestors

IN all the ancient menageries that Georges Cuvier dug out of the Parisian subsoil a century and a half ago, it happened that there was not a trace of prehistoric humans. It seemed plain enough to the great paleontologist that *"l'homme fossile n'existe pas"*—there was no such thing as fossil man. This did not stop people from looking. Here and there, in this old cave and that old river bed, archeologists ran across chipped flints and polished axes, but the bones mixed in with such finds were those of animals, and not manlike. Someone had used the crude tools; yet it never occurred to the finders that some of the pebble implements they collected might actually be older than the human species itself— that tools had been the making of man as well as man being the maker of tools.

Before Cuvier's dictum and after it, some imaginative souls tried to visualize creatures which were more than apes yet not quite men. Tracking down early notions about such missing links, Thomas Huxley found an account written in 1598 by a Portuguese sailor named Eduardo Lopez. "In the Songan country on the banks of the Zaire [Congo]," Lopez related, "are multitudes of apes which afford great delight to the nobles by imitating human gestures." By way of documenting this he had drawn two tailless, long-armed apes, cavorting like clowns

THE FACE:
FROM FISH TO MAN

SHARK

LIZARD

OPOSSUM

LEMUR

—on the same page with a winged, two-legged, crocodile-headed dragon. Huxley was interested but not impressed.

The logical Carl Linnaeus correctly classified man with the mammals—and with what are now called the anthropoids—in his *Systema Naturae* published in 1735. But the illustrations by one of his pupils, in a later book, show that the master had some strange concepts of the anthropoidal order's other members. Several of them combined human heads that could have been copied from a medieval tapestry with bodies as shaggy as a bear's. Another one, hairless except for a circular brush around the face, was drawn with a foot-long tail.

Both extreme versions of man's origins—that he was without earthly predecessors or was endowed with fanciful ones—suffered a rude upset in 1856. In the little Neander Valley near Düsseldorf, Germany, a limestone cave yielded an extraordinary skull fragment and some associated long bones. The skullcap was thick, with massive, lowering ridges over the eyes, and immediate scientific reaction to its discovery was as confused as the case of the five blind men and the elephant. It was clearly manlike—but what kind of a man? Rudolf Virchow, Europe's leading pathologist, dismissed the Neanderthal "man" as a not very ancient pathological idiot. Another physician declared that the deceased had suffered from "hypertrophic deformation." A German authority theorized that the remains were those of "one of the Cossacks who came from Russia in 1814."

Darwin heard about these remarkable bones, yet never investigated them, but Huxley undertook a thorough study of the unprecedented skull. In the condition in which it was discovered, the cranium could hold 63 cubic inches of water; complete, it would have contained 75 cubic inches, or as much as the skulls of living primitive tribesmen. So the brain must have been of modern size too; and the limb bones, though on the bulky side, were "quite those of an European of middle stature. . . ." "Under whatever aspect we view this cranium," wrote Huxley in 1863, in his book *Zoological Evidences as to Man's Place in Nature*, "whether we regard its vertical depression, the enormous thickness of the supraciliary ridges, its sloping occiput, or its long and straight squamosal suture, we meet with apelike characteristics, stamping it as the most pithecoid [apelike] of human crania yet discovered." Neanderthal man, Huxley concluded, was more nearly allied to the higher apes than the latter are to the lower apes, but for all of that he was a man. (A most successful man, as later finds were to prove: he dominated Europe for some 35,000 years until *Homo sapiens*, modern man, took over about 40,000 to 50,000 years ago.) "In some older strata," Huxley wondered, "do the fossilized bones of an ape more anthropoid, or a man more pithecoid, than any yet known await the researches of some unborn paleontologist?"

The question obsessed a young Dutch doctor, Eugène Dubois, who determined that he would be the paleontologist such bones awaited. Dubois reasoned that any in-between form would in all probability have originated either in Africa where the gorilla and chimpanzee still exist, or in Malaya where the orangutan survives. He therefore eagerly accepted an appointment as a surgeon with the Royal Dutch Army in Sumatra. His hopes were high, for Sumatra and neighboring Java had escaped extensive glacial earth-scraping during the ice ages and there was a good prospect that fossils might have been preserved there. Thus Dubois sailed for Padang, Sumatra, in 1887, to seek man's ancestors.

The Sumatra caves where he began his explorations yielded nothing but some teeth of the orangutan, which was then extinct on that island. But word came of the discovery of a very ancient skull at Wadjak in Java. Dubois persuaded the government to send him there to search for "fossil vertebrate fauna." Java, like Sumatra, once had formed a part of the Asiatic mainland. Animals could have wandered down from the north freely and dry of foot. Later the seas had crept in, inundating the lower land and turning the mountaintops into islands.

At Wadjak, Dubois managed to buy the skull of which he had heard, and then promptly found another. But they were not the skulls of the missing link of which he was dreaming; they were too recent. He said nothing about them, and pressed on. At Trinil, roughly in the center of Java, the Solo River was cutting its slow way through a plain covered deep with ashes and tufa from the surrounding volcanoes. In some places the volcanic debris had piled up to a depth of 350 feet. For years the natives had been prying huge ancient bones out of the riverbanks, bones reputed to be those of the giant rakshasas, the spirits which guarded all the temples of Java.

In a stratum about four feet thick and exposed just above the stream level, Dubois in his turn came upon a rich store of animal fossils: a stegodon, an extinct hippopotamus, a small axis deer, an antelope. It was a favorable omen. Soon he also uncovered a fragment of a lower jaw. He felt certain it was human rather than animal. Before he could pursue this highly interesting find, the rains set in and he had to abandon his excavations until the following autumn. In September 1891 he once more set to work. At first he found a right molar tooth that again looked human or near-human. A month later he brushed the earth away from the fossil he had crossed half the world to find, a thick, chocolate-brown cranium. From its resting place of untold millennia Dubois lifted out a piece of a skull unlike any ever seen before. Clearly it was too low and flat to be the cranium of a modern man, and yet in its conformation and other features, it could not be the cranium of an ape.

"The amazing thing had happened," wrote G. Elliot Smith, an English paleontologist. "Dubois had actually found the fossil his scientific imagination had visualized."

But Dubois himself was not so sure. Was this perhaps only the cranium of some unknown, extinct ape? Once more the rains halted his work. The next season he cut a new excavation about 33 feet from where the strange cranium had been buried, and there he found a thigh bone, a femur. As a skilled anatomist, Dubois could tell what it was: an essentially human thigh bone, belonging to a being that had walked upright.

THE implications were staggering. Dubois had to make certain. He studied and measured the apelike skull and the humanlike leg bone, for a momentous decision was forming in his mind. Not until 1894 was he ready to make a public statement of it. Then he announced to the world that the low skull and the human leg bone had belonged to the same creature. Nothing could have been more startling, an apelike head and the upright posture of a man. Deliberately and almost provocatively, Dubois named this creature he had materialized from the past *Pithecanthropus erectus: pithekos* from the Greek for ape, and *anthropos* for man. Some years earlier the German scientist Ernst Haeckel had hypothesized the existence of an in-between creature to which he gave this name. By appropriating it for his Java find, Dubois boldly filed his claim to have found the missing link.

To those unwilling to acknowledge any link with any form of anthropoid ancestor, *Pithecanthropus* was insult added to injury. Clergymen hastened to assure their flocks that Adam, and not the crude, half-ape, half-human brute unearthed

MONKEY

GORILLA

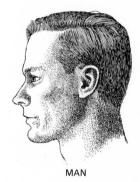

MAN

The development of the face, from the fish to contemporary man, is shown in successive stages. In the lower orders, here represented by the shark, the jaw is simply an underslung mouth, the nose just a snout, the forehead flat and the head long. Progressing through reptiles, marsupials and primates to man, the jaw pushes down and forward, the eyes work their way to the front of the head for true binocular vision. The head becomes increasingly spherical—the most efficient shape for maximum brain in minimum skull.

in Java, was the true ancestor of man. Dubois was denounced from pulpit and platform. Scientists were almost as angry and skeptical. The combination of ape-like head and upright posture ran directly contrary to the belief that the development of a larger, better brain had come first in the separation of the human stock from earlier anthropoids. A being with a human head and an apelike body was expected, not the other way around.

Dubois patiently defended his *Pithecanthropus*. He exhibited the fossil's bones at scientific meetings throughout Europe, presenting detailed measurements and the full data about his discovery. The attacks, nevertheless, did not lessen. Disheartened and hurt, Dubois, by then a professor of geology at the University of Amsterdam, withdrew the remains of *Pithecanthropus* from the public realm. In 1895 he locked the fossils in a strongbox in the Teyler Museum of Haarlem, his home town, and permitted no one to see them for the next 28 years.

In 1920 the discovery of an ancient skull in Australia led scientists to urge that *Pithecanthropus* be let out of solitary confinement, but Dubois was obstinate. In fact, he added to the problem by announcing for the first time that he had the two Wadjak skulls; no one could see them either. At this point Dr. Henry Fairfield Osborn, head of the American Museum of Natural History, appealed to the president of the Dutch Academy of Sciences in the hope that this material, essential to science, would be made available. Soon afterward, in 1923, Dubois opened his strongboxes for Dr. Aleš Hrdlička of the Smithsonian Institution, and thereafter again exhibited *Pithecanthropus* at scientific meetings. Dubois also released a cast of the *Pithecanthropus* skull, indicating a brain of about 900 cubic centimeters, well above the 325- to 685-cubic-centimeter range of the apes, and below the average 1,200 to 1,500 of modern man.

WHILE the bones of Java man lay locked away, a few other fossils of apparently early origin were turning up in other parts of the world. England was filled with excitement and controversy over a remarkable skull and some other fossil fragments unearthed on the Piltdown Common between 1908 and 1915. The Piltdown skull differed radically from that of *Pithecanthropus*. It rounded into almost as high a dome as a modern skull, although the jaw was that of an ape. Thus Piltdown came much closer than *Pithecanthropus* to the prevailing expectations of what early man ought to have looked like.

A young Canadian physician and biologist, Dr. Davidson Black, went to England at about this time to study and to assist with the restoration of the Piltdown skull—a find which many years later embarrassingly turned out to be a hoax. The work deepened Black's already ardent interest in the history and background of man. He thought that man might well have originated in Asia, and when he was offered an appointment as professor of anatomy at Peking Union Medical College, he eagerly accepted. It would place him on the scene.

At first, though, Black's careful investigations yielded nothing. Not a trace of early man could be found on the whole great continent until Dr. J. G. Andersson, a Swedish geologist, walked into Black's office one day with two teeth an associate had found protruding from a rock face at Choukoutien. For centuries the Chinese had been mining "dragon bones" in the clefts of the hill. When pulverized they made a prized medicine. As Black examined the teeth from this reputed repository of ancient monsters, his hopes soared. He was certain that they came from a human of great antiquity. The Rockefeller Foundation also was impressed. At Black's urging the foundation agreed to finance a full-scale scientific exploration of Choukoutien.

The hill reared its low, rounded crest about 40 miles southwest of Peking. Just below it lay the little village of Choukoutien, and beyond that the wide expanse of the Hopei plain, crossed by both a modern railroad and the old sunken road along which camels plodded their slow way to the city. At some remote time in the past, water had honeycombed the limestone of the hill with caves and fissures. The caves in turn had filled with the deposits of running water and with the debris of collapsing roofs. By the 20th Century, when modern quarrying cut away one face of the hill, the former caves appeared only as clefts, or in some cases as hard dikes, or solidified fills.

It was here in 1927 that the first scientific expedition in the search for man's origins began its spadework. Digging in the hard, compacted stone proved difficult; blasting was often necessary. Just as much of a problem was the troubled political condition of China. Antiforeign riots were flaring and Chiang Kai-shek's armies, moving to the relief of Shanghai, still were far from the city. Bandits controlled the countryside around Peking. For weeks at a time they isolated the dig from the city.

Three days before the first season's work was to end, Dr. Birgir Bohlin, field supervisor, found another early human tooth. As he hurried to Peking to take it to Black, soldiers stopped him several times without suspecting that he carried a scientific treasure in his pocket. Black pored over the new tooth night after night. It differed so markedly from all the others in his large collection of casts that he decided upon a bold step. He set up a new genus and species for the man from whom it came—*Sinanthropus pekinensis* (Chinese man of Peking). It was a large classification to be based on one small tooth, and the scientific world reserved judgment.

The work in 1928 and through most of 1929 yielded more than 1,000 boxes of fossil animal bones, a few additional human teeth and several small fragments of human bone. By December 2 the weather was bitingly cold and the work was about to be closed for the year, when Dr. W. C. Pei opened up two caves at the extreme end of the fissure. On the floor of one was a large accumulation of debris. Pei brushed some of it away, and suddenly there lay revealed the object of all their work and searching, a nearly complete skullcap. It was partly surrounded by loose sand and partly embedded in travertine, a water-formed rock. Even at first glance, Pei felt certain that it was a skullcap of *Sinanthropus*. He rushed the momentous news to Black.

A t a dinner party on the night of December 7, 1929, the night after the skull reached Peking, Black whispered to Roy Chapman Andrews, the American scientist: "Roy, we've got a skull! Pei found it December second." As soon as the two men could get away, they hurried to Black's laboratory. "There it was, the skull of an individual who had lived half a million years ago," Andrews wrote. "It was one of the most important discoveries in the whole history of human evolution. He could not have been very impressive when he was alive, but dead and fossilized, he was awe-inspiring."

The news made headlines all around the world. The work at the hill then was reorganized on a broader basis, and in the 1930s the pieces of a second *Sinanthropus* skull came to light. Black continued to work day and night, organizing the work, keeping detailed records of all the finds, classifying, making casts, drawings and photographs of the heavy volume of material pouring into Peking. He suffered a heart attack one day as he was climbing around the hill at Choukoutien. Without saying anything about the seriousness of his condition, he made

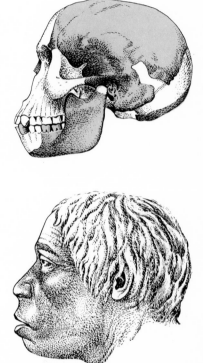

The Piltdown man puzzled anthropologists for decades because he combined a chimpanzeelike jaw and teeth with fragments of a human skull. Not until 1953 did scientists prove conclusively that the fossil was a hoax perpetrated by Charles Dawson, an English amateur biologist. Dawson had artfully put together unrelated fragments found in a gravel bed near the Piltdown Common in England, and claimed the discovery of a missing link.

STEPS IN RECONSTRUCTING A FOSSIL HEAD

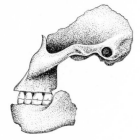

ORIGINAL FRAGMENT

The reconstruction of a fossil head is a three-dimensional jigsaw puzzle in which bone fragments (such as those above) are pieced together, and layers of clay to simulate muscles, tissues and skin added until a facsimile of the original is obtained.

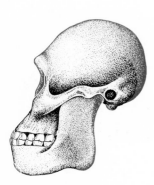

RECONSTRUCTED SKULL

In the first stage of fossil reconstruction, the molder extends the contours indicated by the original fragments by adding clay (red) to the skull. The more extensive the original fragment, the less work there is and the more accurate the representation.

plans for the next season and put his affairs in order. Death came to the dedicated scientist in 1934.

The Rockefeller Foundation sought carefully for a successor. It found him in Dr. Franz Weidenreich, then a visiting professor of anatomy at the University of Chicago. Before the Nazis drove him from his native Germany, Weidenreich had completed world-famous studies of the evolutionary changes in the pelvis and foot that made possible man's upright posture. His studies underwrote the contention of Darwin and Huxley that man is a descendant of some ancient anthropoid stock, but not of any recent genus of one.

IN China, Weidenreich began a classic series of studies of Peking man—*The Dentition of Sinanthropus*, *The Extremity Bones of Sinanthropus*, *The Skull of Sinanthropus*. All three scientifically supported the conclusion of Black: *Sinanthropus* was indeed a human, though a very primitive one. He was not a link between apes and men. What placed him solidly in the human race was his undoubted ability to walk upright on two legs. "Apes, like man, have two hands and two feet, but man alone has acquired an upright position and the faculty of using his feet exclusively as locomotor instruments," said Weidenreich. "Unless all signs are deceiving, the claim may even be ventured that the change in locomotion and the corresponding alteration of the organization of the body are the essential specialization in the transformation of the prehuman form into the human form."

The teeth and dental arch of *Sinanthropus* testified further to his status. The canines were not the projecting fangs of the ape; they did not come together like the blades of a pair of scissors. And the dental arch was curved, not oblong. Still another proof lay in the skull. Weidenreich arranged the skulls of a gorilla, of Peking man and of modern man in an enlightening, haunting row. Even a glance revealed their striking differences: the extremely flat skull of the gorilla, the somewhat higher skull of Peking man, the rounded skull of modern man. In the low pate of the gorilla a brain of about 450 cubic centimeters was housed; in the higher dome of Peking man, one of about 1,000 cubic centimeters; and in the high cranium of modern man, a brain of about 1,350 cubic centimeters.

With a brain so small, some scientists questioned the human status of Peking man. Weidenreich cautioned that brain size alone is no absolute determinant, pointing out that one species of whale has a brain of about 10,000 cubic centimeters. But this amounts to one gram of brain for each 8,500 grams of body weight, compared to man's one gram for each 44 grams of weight. "Neither the absolute nor the relative size of the brain can be used to measure the degree of mental ability in animals or man," he added. "Cultural objects are the only guide as far as spiritual life is concerned. They may be fallacious guides too, but we are completely lost if these objects are missing."

At Choukoutien cultural objects were not missing. The continuing excavations produced thousands of chipped-stone tools. They were simple, with only a few chips removed, but they were made to a pattern. Some of them lay with charred bits of wood and bone. And the charring did not result from some accidental fire, for hard-baked red and yellow clay—hearths, that is—often underlay the carbon. Peking man had mastered the use of fire.

The bones of thousands of animals were strewn about in the former caves. More than three quarters of them belonged to deer, which must have been the favorite meat of Peking man. There also were bones of the bighorn sheep, the boar, the bison, the ostrich, and even of such river dwellers as the otter. All of the mammalian bones came from species long since gone from the earth. About 20 feet below the lowest outer threshold of the big cave, the expedition also found Peking man's garbage dump, by now a stony amalgam of thousands of scraps of bone, stone chips and hackberry seeds. All in all, by his fires and his handiwork as well as by his bodily structure, Peking man indubitably established his right to a place in the human family.

Soon after the big excavations began in China, the Geological Survey of the Netherlands East Indies invited a young German paleontologist, G.H.R. von Koenigswald, to resume the search for early man in Java. On an upper terrace of the same Solo River whose banks had harbored the bones of Dubois' *Pithecanthropus*, Von Koenigswald in 1937 found fragments of 11 somewhat more recent "Solo skulls," and in a region to the west, called Sangiran, the skull of another *Pithecanthropus*. At first only a few pieces of the latter were found. Von Koenigswald offered his native helpers 10 cents for each additional piece they could discover. When it was all assembled, the second skull could scarcely have been more like the first. "It was a little eerie," said Von Koenigswald, "to come upon two skulls . . . which resembled each other as much as two eggs."

In 1939 Von Koenigswald went to Peking to compare the Java finds with those from Choukoutien. Again two widely separated discoveries proved conspicuously alike. "In its general form and size [the Peking skull] agrees with the Java skull to such an extent that it identifies *Pithecanthropus* too as true man and a creature far above the stage of an ape," said Weidenreich, upsetting the judgment of Dubois that *Pithecanthropus* came before man.

The first judgment of the men in the field was later corroborated by Wilfrid E. Le Gros Clark, professor of anatomy at the University of Oxford. *Pithecanthropus* appeared slightly more primitive, with his brain of about 900 cubic centimeters, and a shade heavier jaw. The animals he killed and ate also were a little older than those at Peking and no tools were found with *Pithecanthropus*. Despite these differences the two were strikingly alike.

Von Koenigswald and Weidenreich agreed that Java man and Peking man differed little more than "two different races of present mankind," and Clark came to the same conclusion. The Oxford authority proposed dropping the *Sinanthropus* classification which said the Peking man constituted another genus. It was doubtful that the two even formed separate species. Clark therefore suggested that both should be identified as *Pithecanthropus*, and distinguished only by their place names, *Pithecanthropus erectus* of Java, and *Pithecanthropus pekinensis*, or more simply as Java man and Peking man.

THE modern world was about to prove too hazardous for these early men emerging from the long-hidden reaches of the past. By the autumn of 1941 the scientists working at Choukoutien could not misread the signs of war. There were daily reports of Japanese troop movements. Weidenreich was in the United States on a visit, but the director of the Geological Survey appealed to Dr. Henry S. Houghton, president of Peking Union Medical College, to have the irreplaceable remains of Peking man taken to safety. Dr. Houghton was doubtful that the United States should assume responsibility, but nevertheless arranged to have the collection taken to the United States with a Marine detachment that was leaving by special train in a few days.

At 5 a.m. on December 5 the train pulled out of Peking. It was to meet the American liner *President Harrison* at the small coastal town of Chingwangtao. This rendezvous was never kept, for on December 7 Japanese bombs crashed

DEEP-MUSCLE ADDITION

Next the molding artist—who must have a solid understanding of anatomy—uses more clay to form the deep muscles, which are attached to the original bone and to the newly reconstructed parts. Old muscle markings on the original bone guide him.

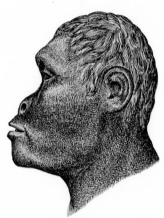

FINISHED HEAD

After clay for the fatty tissue has been added to the tip of the nose, the chin and to the ears, the skin covering is applied. However, details like the distribution and amount of hair and minute surface configurations can only be assumed by the artist.

down on Pearl Harbor and total war came violently to the Pacific. In the maelstrom, all that existed of Peking man—fossil pieces representing about 40 individuals—disappeared, never to be seen again.

In Java, Von Koenigswald knew that it was only a matter of time until the island would be seized. So he quietly gave some of his most valuable fossils to friends and substituted casts for them in his museum. Soon after the occupation of Java, Von Koenigswald, his wife and daughter were sent to separate concentration camps. The Japanese became suspicious about the fossil collection, but never discovered the truth. On the whole they took good care of the museum, for they expected to keep it after winning the war, and they understood its value. Only one skull was removed, one of the Solo skulls, which was sent as a special birthday gift to the Emperor of Japan.

At the end of the war, Von Koenigswald learned that his wife and daughter were safe. "My happiness was complete," he said, "when I learned that my precious specimens had been saved. Large parts of my collections, many of my books, and all of my clothes had been stolen, but Early Man had survived the disaster." Von Koenigswald later exhibited Java man in New York and then took the precious bones to The Netherlands, where he became professor of paleontology and historical geology at the State University of Utrecht.

With the end of the war, the second search for Peking man began. Three nations joined it, but the story of what happened to the fossils in December 1941 has never been clarified. It is certain only that the *President Harrison* was beached to prevent its seizure and that the Japanese captured the special train. One account holds that the Japanese loaded the small remains of Peking man on a lighter for transfer to a Japanese ship, and that the lighter sank.

It is unlikely that any Japanese who recognized the uniqueness of the collection came into possession of it. After the occupation of Peking the Japanese ransacked the city searching for Peking man. "They knew what they were looking for, and knew that the relics had been in Peking," said Miss Agnes Pearce, secretary of the China Medical Board. "The controller of the college was taken into custody and questioned for five days."

On the chance that Peking man might have been taken secretly to Japan, the Looted Properties Division of the Far East Command combed Japan for his bones. The Communist government of China in its turn took up the search. No trace was found, but Dr. Pei, the finder of the first skull, broadcast the charge that the United States was secreting the remains of Peking man at the American Museum of Natural History in New York. Dr. Harry L. Shapiro, chairman of the museum's Department of Anthropology, pointed out in answer that the museum has only casts of the Peking fossils. Weidenreich had made them and sent them to a number of museums before the start of World War II.

THE fate of Peking man remains one of the great international mysteries, but his standing is secure. However fleeting and violent his reappearance, his bones and those of Java man offered incontrovertible proof of mankind's lengthy existence. These ancestors emerging from the past were not what their descendants expected them to be, for they were crude, primitive and low of brow. But they walked like men, they were intelligent, and they lived successfully in their environments of 360,000 years ago. They were men, not forms transitional between animals and men. Huxley's haunting question still had to be answered: was there in some older strata an ape more anthropoid or a man more pithecoid than any yet known?

A ZOO-KEPT GORILLA TOYS WITH HER NEWBORN BABY. LIKE HUMAN MOTHERS, GORILLAS HAVE A LONG, CLOSE MOTHER-CHILD RELATIONSHIP

The Manlike Great Apes

Human kinship to the great apes is very close. The face and form of man and the gorilla, seemingly cast in the same rough mold, recall a common ancestral origin. Today scientists are learning that this man-ape parallel carries over to group behavior as well. Our jungle cousins are highly developed social beings living in tribal organizations probably similar in many respects to those of primitive man.

FRIGHTENED FAMILY scrambles to the top of a flimsy tree to escape white hunters. Under ordinary circumstances the heavy gorilla avoids climbing trees except to sleep in low branches.

A GARGANTUAN MOTHER suckles a puny youngster in a jungle bower. Gorillas are very solicitous of their young and have been known to risk their lives unhesitatingly to protect their children.

The Family-Minded Gorilla

Among the great apes only the gorilla joined man to take up a life primarily oriented to the ground. Giving up tree-climbing except as an emergency means of escaping danger *(top left)*, it lost the great nimbleness of other primates. In compensation the gorilla acquired vast strength and size—the average full-grown male weighs over a quarter of a ton. It also developed exceptional family cohesiveness which provided the best protection of all from its enemies. In this last respect the gorilla tended to follow an evolutionary course very similar to primitive man's.

Rarely are gorillas found living by themselves in the wild. As a rule they move in small family troops that remain together the whole year round. Dominated by one adult male, the troop generally is made up of two or more "wives" plus a number of younger male hangers-on. Sometimes a couple of families band together into a single unit. When the females are carrying young, the males are in constant attendance. If any danger threatens, the leader puts on a frightening show of might *(bottom left)*, beating its chest and bellowing loudly. Gorillas seldom have to threaten much further to scare off predators.

POUNDING ITS CHEST, a male rages at an intruder. With this intimidation display it emits a loud guttural noise peculiar to gorillas. Rarely, it follows this with a charge.

OFF TO BED goes a huge male gorilla, carrying under one arm a shock of leaves and branches to be used for bedding. Although they are constantly on the move in the jungle, gorillas take time each night to build elaborate nests to sleep in on the ground or in low tree branches. These are used only once. Some of the nesting material may serve as food for the vegetarian gorilla.

The Patriarchal Chimpanzees

Chimpanzees seem easily the most human of the great apes. Tests of laboratory animals show them to be amazingly adept at picking up human skills. In their native habitat, as shown in these rare pictures of wild chimpanzees, they exhibit another remarkable similarity to man in the manner in which they live together. As sociable as the gorillas, chimpanzees go around in even larger troops. Groups of females with young band together with a couple of males, while childless females consort with other males in separate troops. Recalling the pattern of many early human societies, chimpanzee troops are guided not by the biggest and toughest male but by the oldest and wisest. One of these wizened patriarchs is pictured here.

A question that the intelligent, social chimpanzee poses is what prevented it from developing further along human lines. The answer may be man himself. Anthropologists surmise that in the competition for survival the chimpanzee was forced, possibly by early man's invention of the spear, to remain a jungle animal, a fact that retarded its development.

GRIZZLED ELDER of a chimpanzee band feeds on the fruit of the papaw tree, a favorite chimpanzee staple. Silvered hair and a bent back indicate that this ape may be over 40 years old.

DOZING MOTHER has a sheltering arm about her child while she is asleep. Throughout the chimpanzee's long infancy she keeps the child close to her, nursing it up to a year or more.

ALERT FOR DANGER, a cautious troop reconnoiters a jungle clearing. The leader is the graying animal at left, which acts as a security inspector for the band. Though infirm with age, it is indulged and catered to by even the strongest males out of respect for its superior knowledge of jungle dangers. In other ape societies, like the gorillas', such old males are usually killed off.

EATING ON THE RUN, a chimpanzee eats a papaw held in one hand, while its free hand half-supports its weight on the ground. Primarily vegetarian, chimpanzees sometimes eat meat, too.

FACING ITS ENEMY, a club-wielding ape charges toward a leopard in a controlled experiment. Some scientists think this kind of test proves that chimpanzees use weapons instinctively.

SUCKLING A CHILD, a female baboon has her coat groomed by another female. Removing each other's parasites in this fashion is a freely exchanged service among the highly sociable baboons.

The Highly Sociable Baboons

If a baboon separates from its troop its chances of survival drop almost to zero. More than any other apes, baboons have become dependent on banding together to protect themselves and rear their young. A lion is reared by its mother to be self-sufficient; by contrast a baboon is brought up to take its proper place in the social order of its troop.

The history of such a childhood recalls in many ways the bringing-up of primitive man. During a one- to three-year period of babyhood the baboon child very rarely leaves its mother, clinging to her fur or riding on her back (*opposite*). Then comes a period in which it becomes part of a play-group of other juvenile baboons with whom it practices the rudiments of grown-up social behavior. The young baboon develops special friendships at this time that may last for years. After puberty, the males find their places in the adult hierarchy of strength and take on responsibility for defending the troop. The females become mothers and then with their infants are the primary objects of troop protection.

WATCHFUL BABOONS FEED TOGETHER WITH ANIMALS OF THE AFRICAN SAVANNA FOR MUTUAL DEFENSE AGAINST LIONS. PROTECTED BY THE SHARP

PICKABACK BABY chews on a grass blade while riding precariously on its mother. Except for knowing how to cling and suckle, the baboon infant is born helpless; all the behavior patterns of the troop must be learned from the mother. The young baboon has great magnetism for the other troop members, who continually cluster around the mother, grooming her and the child.

HEARING OF THE BABOONS AND THE SENSE OF SMELL OF THE IMPALAS (CENTER, FOREGROUND), SUCH A GROUP IS DIFFICULT TO TAKE BY SURPRISE

ANCESTRAL PRIMATE, the big-eyed tarsier hunts by night for small lizards and insects in the treetops of Indonesia and the Philippines. About 50 million years ago, its forebears ranged the globe, and may have occupied a rung on the evolutionary ladder between more primitive lemurs and monkeys, apes and men.

7

Dawn Man and His Brothers

Dr. Raymond A. Dart, professor of anatomy at South Africa's University of Witwatersrand, impatiently pried the lid off a big wooden box of rocks that had just been delivered at his Johannesburg home. He hoped the rough fragments inside the box might include a fossil baboon skull. And luck was with him, for on the very top of the heap lay the cast, or mold, of the interior of a skull. Such a fossilized "brain cast" of any species of ape would have been a notable discovery, but this one was no ordinary anthropoidal brain. It was three times as big as a baboon's and larger than that of an adult chimpanzee. When he came to a chunk of rock into which the cast fitted perfectly, the tremendous thought struck Dart that he might be holding the missing link in his hands.

The box had come from a limestone quarry near Taung, a railroad station not far from Johannesburg. A rare fossil baboon skull had been found there recently, and by way of cooperating with science, the quarry operator had agreed to ship any bone-bearing rock to the doctor. Dart's first problem was to free the rest of the strange, larger skull from the stone matrix. Working with a hammer, chisels and a sharpened knitting needle, he "pecked, scraped, and levered" bits of stone from the front of the skull and the eye sockets.

After days of this painstaking dissection an incredible face began to emerge. It was not surmounted by the beetling brow of an ape but by a true forehead, and the upper jaw, instead of jutting forward as in all true apes, was shortened and retracted under the skull. Was this ape, or man, or both? From then on, Dart lay awake nights "in a fever of thoughts" about what kind of ape might have lived long ago in this semidesert plateau. For more than 70 million years, while ice had advanced and retreated over much of the earth and while mountains rose along the continental coasts, South Africa had stood as a dry, relatively undisturbed veld, much as it is today. It had never been clothed with the kind of jungle in which an ape could live, and the nearest natural habitat of apes was more than 2,000 miles away from Taung. Could some different kind of ape have found a way to adapt itself to life in an arid, open land?

Dart was up daily at dawn to continue his exacting labor with the baffling skull. On his 73rd day of work the stone parted and he saw before him the skull of a six-year-old child with a full set of milk teeth. The permanent molars were just beginning to erupt and the canines, as in humans, were quite small. The set of the skull indicated that this child had walked upright. No ape can take more than a few steps without going down on all fours.

ALL previous discoveries of human predecessors had proved in the end to be men—authentic, if early, men. This was true of the thick-skulled but large-brained Neanderthal man, of Java man, of Peking man. All were men with certain apelike features. But the child's face before Dart seemed the reverse, an ape with human features. He set up a new genus for it, with the formidable name *Australopithecus africanus* (*Austral*, for south, and *pithekos*, for ape). Dart wrote a full scientific report for the February 3, 1925, issue of the British magazine *Nature*. It included the provocative statement, "The specimen is of importance because it exhibits an extinct race of apes intermediate between living anthropoids and man." He agreed to release the news to the Johannesburg *Star* on the same date. At the last moment *Nature* decided it could not publish so startling an article without referring it to experts for comment. The *Star* would wait no longer, so on that day, in South Africa and around the world, the headlines proclaimed that the missing link was found. Actually it was the first link in a long chain of discoveries in which Africa, and not the Middle East or Asia, would be established as the presumed birthplace of the human race.

The attacks on Dart were not long in coming. Such English authorities as Sir Arthur Keith, Elliot Smith and Sir Arthur Smith Woodward expressed skepticism and disagreement. Dart's "baby," several critics suggested, was only "the distorted skull of a chimpanzee." Taung became something of a byword; it figured in songs and was heard on every music-hall stage. But Dart was encouraged by a warm letter of congratulation. It came from Dr. Robert Broom, a Scottish physician who had hunted fossils all over the world before being drawn to Africa by reports of the finding of mammallike reptiles. In the Karroo, Broom had unearthed fossils that almost completely filled the gap between the egg-laying reptiles and the small early mammals. His researches were called "as masterly as any in the century" by the scholarly prime minister of South Africa, Field Marshal Jan C. Smuts. Two weeks after the arrival of his letter, Broom showed up at Dart's laboratory. He spent a weekend in intensive study of the child's skull, and was convinced that as "a connecting link between the higher apes and one of the lowest human types," it was the most important fossil find made up to that time. He firmly said so in an article in *Nature*.

However, after the first flare-up of attention, Dart's "baby" was either forgotten or dismissed by most scientists. Still Dart and Broom continued to study the skull. In 1929 Dart succeeded in separating the lower jaw from the upper, and for the first time was able to see the entire pattern of the teeth. Most of them could have belonged to a child of today, though the molars were larger. In the minds of the two physicians any lingering doubts were removed.

Broom was eager to take up the search for another *Australopithecus*, an adult one. It would be the only way, he was sure, to dissolve the disbelief. Smuts opened the way by offering Broom a post as curator of vertebrate paleontology and physical anthropology at the Transvaal Museum in Pretoria. For the next 18 months Broom was occupied in digging out and identifying half a dozen extinct species of rats and moles. He also unearthed a baboon jaw which at first appeared to be australopithecine. It was not, but the publicity led two students of Dart's to tell Broom about some small skulls they had found in a quarry at Sterkfontein, a town not far from Pretoria. Broom arranged to go there with them.

Ever since the first mining camps were opened during the Witwatersrand gold rush of 1886, the people of the Sterkfontein area had been picking up the fossilized remains of baboons, monkeys and perhaps, unknowingly, ape men. The limeworks had even issued a little guidebook, "Come to Sterkfontein and Find the Missing Link." Dr. Broom came on August 9, 1936, and promptly did so. G. W. Barlow, the quarry manager, had formerly worked at Taung and knew about the australopithecine skull. When Broom asked if he had ever seen anything like it at Sterkfontein, Barlow said he "rather thought" he had. He explained that he usually sold "any nice bones or skulls" to Sunday visitors to the quarry. He promised Broom that he would keep a sharp lookout for anything resembling an ape-man skull.

Nine days later when Broom returned, Barlow asked, "Is this what you're after?" and handed him two thirds of a "beautiful fossil brain cast." It had been blasted out only that morning. Broom anxiously dug into the debris to try to find the skull that had served as the mold. Though he worked until dark, he found nothing. The next day, as he sorted the piles of stone, he not only recovered the base of the skull and both sides of the upper jaw, but also fragments of the brain case. When the fragments were pieced together, Broom had most of the skull of an adult australopithecine.

For three years the doctor continued to visit his fossil gold mine. One June day in 1938, Barlow met him with, "I have something nice for you this morning." He handed Broom an ape-man upper jaw with one molar in place. He had obtained it from a schoolboy, Gert Terblanche, who lived on a farm at Kromdraai, less than a mile away. The doctor drove over to Kromdraai. Gert was at school, but his mother and sister showed Broom the hillside where he had found the fossil piece. The doctor hurried on to the school and found Gert. At his first questions, the boy pulled out of his pocket "four of the most beautiful teeth ever found in the world's history." Back at the site, Gert opened his private cache and gave the doctor an excellent piece of a lower jaw. During the next two days, Broom and the boy sifted earth and found a number of scraps of bone and teeth. When the pieces were put together, Broom had most of another ape-man skull, the third. The face was flatter than the Sterkfontein *Australopithecus'*, the jaw heavier and the teeth larger, though more human in conformation.

When the newest findings were published, some of the old skepticism began to dissipate. Kromdraai man differed so markedly from both the Taung child

**DIGGING FOR HISTORY
IN AN ANCIENT CAVE**

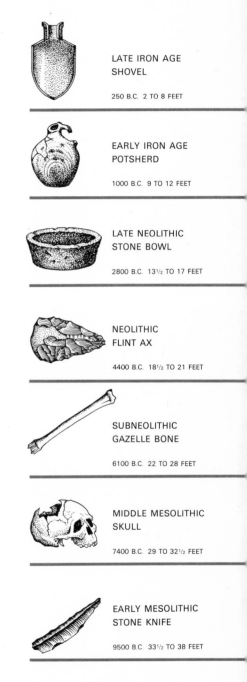

LATE IRON AGE
SHOVEL

250 B.C. 2 TO 8 FEET

EARLY IRON AGE
POTSHERD

1000 B.C. 9 TO 12 FEET

LATE NEOLITHIC
STONE BOWL

2800 B.C. 13½ TO 17 FEET

NEOLITHIC
FLINT AX

4400 B.C. 18½ TO 21 FEET

SUBNEOLITHIC
GAZELLE BONE

6100 B.C. 22 TO 28 FEET

MIDDLE MESOLITHIC
SKULL

7400 B.C. 29 TO 32½ FEET

EARLY MESOLITHIC
STONE KNIFE

9500 B.C. 33½ TO 38 FEET

More than 11,000 years of human history have been unearthed at the Hotu cave on the shores of the Caspian Sea in Iran. In 1951 a team of archeologists headed by an American, Dr. Carleton S. Coon, excavated some 38 feet below the cave floor to discover, at various levels, artifacts and bones from seven separate cultures. These remarkable finds, which have been carefully carbon-dated, indicate the narrow Caspian corridor was a busy route for early man's migrations to and from Asia.

THE EVOLUTION
OF MAN'S SKULL

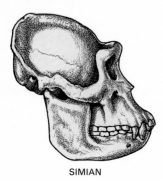

SIMIAN

*The skull of a gorilla bears a superficial re-
semblance to that of man, but its brain
capacity is only about 450 c.c. The thick
bony crest on top serves as a support for
the muscles that are needed to open and
close the heavy jaw laden with large teeth.*

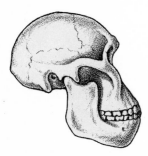

AUSTRALOPITHECUS

*Though basically simian in appearance,
the skull of Australopithecus, an extinct
African ape man that walked upright and
may have used tools, lacks the large, sharp
canine teeth of the gorilla. The brain capacity ranged from about 450 to 650 c.c.*

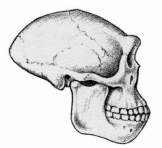

PITHECANTHROPUS IV

*This primitive man had a brain capac-
ity of 900 c.c. As man's jaw became lighter and his teeth smaller, there was more
space for the tongue. And because lighter
muscles operated the lighter jaw, the skull
could become thinner and the brain larger.*

and the Sterkfontein adult that Broom set up a new genus for him, *Paranthropus robustus* (robust near-man). But the claim again upset his fellow scientists. Broom was thought to be going beyond all bounds in setting up another genus for one small African area.

"Of course the critics did not know the whole of the facts," said Broom. "When one has jealous opponents one does not let them know everything." What he had not disclosed was that each of the skulls was associated with its own distinctive set of animals. Ancient horses abounded at Kromdraai. None occurred at Sterkfontein, only a mile away. At Kromdraai, Broom found the bones of jackals, baboons and saber-toothed tigers. The Sterkfontein quarry yielded an extinct wart hog. None was to be found at Kromdraai. If the sites were occupied at different times, Taung some two million years ago, Sterkfontein about 1,200,000 and Kromdraai 800,000, the doctor pointed out, each might well have a different group of extinct animals—and a different genus of ape man.

At this point, World War II halted work at the South African sites. Broom and his assistant, G.W.H. Schepers, made use of the war years to study, meas- ure and describe the astounding volume of material they had collected. After more than 20 years of ignoring or deriding the South African creatures with their astonishing mixture of ape and human characteristics, science was brought to with a shock by a book published by Broom and Schepers. Their data left almost no question that the fossils were near-men, representing an important stage in the evolution of humanity. Exactly what their position might be— ancestors or cousins—still remained moot.

SOON after the end of the war, Broom resumed digging at Sterkfontein. One day a blast in some seemingly unpromising cave debris revealed the first of a series of important discoveries. When the smoke cleared away, the upper half of a perfect skull sparkled brilliantly in the sunlight striking the pinkish-gray stone of the quarry. Lime crystals incrusting its inner surface caught and reflect- ed the light like diamonds. The lower half lay embedded in a block of stone that had broken away. The glittering skull was that of an adult female. Her jaw was heavy, her forehead low, but there was an unmistakable quality of humanness about her. Her discovery was a worldwide sensation. It was followed by other important finds: a male jaw with an intact canine tooth worn down in line with the other teeth as the canines are in men, and then in 1948 a nearly perfect pel- vis. If the pelvis belonged to an ape man, he had walked upright, like man. Other finds confirmed this posture many times over.

By 1949 the remains of more than 30 individuals had been recovered from the South African caves, and Le Gros Clark at Oxford undertook an impartial, definitive study. He meticulously studied the South African fossils themselves, and compared them to a series of 90 skulls of modern apes. His verdict was un- qualified: "It is evident that in some respects they [the Australopithecinae] were definitely ape-like creatures, with small brains and large jaws.

"But in the details of the construction of the skull, in their dental morphology, and in their limb bones, the simian features are combined with a number of characters in which they differ from recent or fossil apes and at the same time approximate quite markedly to the *Hominidae* [the family of man]. All those who have had the opportunity of examining the original material are agreed on these hominid characters: the real issue to be decided is the question of their evolutionary and taxonomic significance."

Were the ape men among the direct ancestors of *Homo sapiens?* The evolutionary question to which Le Gros Clark referred was complicated by the absence of cultural objects—tools—which Franz Weidenreich had pointed out are essential to determining human status. Not one chipped-stone tool had been found with the numerous remains of the ape men. Then in 1953 on a terrace in the Vaal valley laid down in the same dry period in which the ape men lived, some simple pebble tools were discovered—fist-sized pieces of stone from which a few chips had been removed. It seemed impossible that the australopithecines, with their brains of only 450 to 650 cubic centimeters, no larger than those of the apes, could have made them.

Once again, evidence dispelled doubt. In the spring of 1957, pebble tools were found in the upper part of australopithecine debris at Sterkfontein, and a little later J. T. Robinson, who had succeeded Dr. Broom, and Revil Mason dug into a layer of red-brown rock which contained several ape-men teeth and more than 200 pebble tools. To the untrained eye they would have looked like naturally fractured stone. But close examination showed that chips had been flaked off two sides; the head of the stone was left round. A hammer stone held in a hand and guided by understanding had shaped them to perform certain tasks of cutting, scraping and, probably, killing. And the tools were not made of the same stone as the caves where they lay buried. The pebbles had been carried there, purposefully, from some other place.

It appeared that even before they learned to *make* tools, the ape men may have been tool-users. In 1947 Dr. Dart, after 18 years as dean of the Faculty of Medicine at the university, returned to the search for "dawn man." Analyzing thousands of fossilized animal bones found in the cave deposits, the discoverer of *Australopithecus* concluded that the ape men had employed tusks and teeth for cutting tools, jaws for saws and scrapers, and leg bones for bludgeons.

"The Australopithecines must have originated as apes that by walking upright became adapted to life in the open country," said Kenneth Page Oakley in his study *Tools Makyth Man.* "There are many reasons to suppose, as Dart, George A. Bartholemew, and others have shown, that the earliest hominids must have been tool *users.* Bipedalism is initially disadvantageous biologically unless there is some compensating factor—in the case of the hominids this was the ability to use tools and wield weapons while moving. . . . The earliest tools and weapons would have been improvisations with whatever lay ready to hand. Although the hominids must have begun as occasional tool users, ultimately they were only able to survive in the face of rigorous natural selection by developing a system of communication among themselves which enabled cultural tradition to take the place of heredity. At this point systematic tool making replaced casual tool using, and it may be that this changeover took place in the Australopithecine stage."

FAR to the north and east of the desert land of the australopithecines, in Tanganyika's Olduvai Gorge, Louis S. B. Leakey also was finding pebble tools. He first came upon them in 1931, long before they were discovered in South Africa, and wondered if they could have been made by a creature similar to the australopithecines. If so, Leakey was unable to find him. In vain he searched the clearly stacked strata of the gorge for the maker of the tools.

Olduvai Gorge is an abrupt rent in the earth, some 25 miles long and 300 feet deep, a "little Grand Canyon." A German entomologist named Wilhelm Kattwinkel found it in 1911 when he almost fell into its depths as he broke through some bush on the edge. A hasty exploration showed it to be a store-

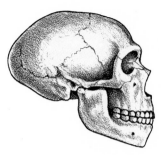

NEANDERTHAL

The profile of a Neanderthal skull shows a retreating forehead, heavy eyebrow ridges and an elongated brain case, which varied in size from 1,400 c.c. to 1,600 c.c. The chin, though sloping, is less muzzlelike than that of more primitive forms of man.

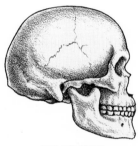

CRO-MAGNON

Cro-Magnon's skull approaches modern man's in appearance, but has an even larger brain capacity—approximately 1,590 c.c. as compared to 1,500 c.c. for the average European. Its high forehead contrasts with the depressed one of Neanderthal man.

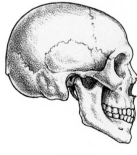

MODERN

Modern man's skull houses evolution's finest product—a richly convoluted, intelligent brain. It is believed that the brain, in continuing to evolve, will grow larger and that the man of the future will have a brain capacity of at least 2,000 c.c.

THE EVOLUTION
OF STONE AGE TOOLS

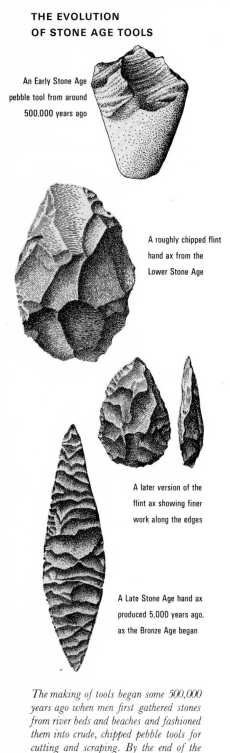

An Early Stone Age
pebble tool from around
500,000 years ago

A roughly chipped flint
hand ax from the
Lower Stone Age

A later version of the
flint ax showing finer
work along the edges

A Late Stone Age hand ax
produced 5,000 years ago,
as the Bronze Age began

The making of tools began some 500,000 years ago when men first gathered stones from river beds and beaches and fashioned them into crude, chipped pebble tools for cutting and scraping. By the end of the period, just prior to the metal ages, primitive men had learned to make delicately wrought hand axes and other tools flaked from a variety of materials, including obsidian, flint—which was sometimes mined from pits and seams—bones and wood.

house of fossils. Some which Kattwinkel took back to Berlin were so unusual that a German expedition headed by Hans Reck was sent out in 1913 to explore further. Its investigations were ended by the First World War, and after the war Reck was unable to raise funds to resume operations. Eventually he wrote to Leakey, the young curator of the Coryndon Memorial Museum at Nairobi, urging him to take over.

The search for early man was one to which Leakey was already dedicated. He was born, in 1903, in a wattle hut near Kabete. His parents were the first missionaries to the Kikuyu tribe, and Leakey was the first white baby most of the tribesmen had ever seen. As Leakey grew up with Kikuyu playmates, he thought of himself as one of them. Sent to England to school and college, Leakey wrote his Cambridge thesis on the Stone Age in Kenya. He returned to Africa in 1924 on an archeological expedition, and later was appointed curator of the Coryndon museum. Not until 1931, however, could he raise the funds for an expedition to Olduvai. It took seven days to cover the 500 miles from Nairobi to the gorge, a wild place frequented by inquisitive lions.

One season was enough to convince Leakey that Olduvai was a site "such as no other in the world." Pebble tools were so abundant at the bottom of the gorge and in its lowest exposed strata that Leakey named their type Oldowan, after the place of their discovery. In these old strata too lay the bones of many extinct animals; ultimately Leakey identified more than 100.

LEAKEY returned to the gorge year after year, and on later expeditions took along his wife and their two sons. They could seldom spend more than seven weeks a year there. The trips were costly, the heat intense, and water had to be hauled from a spring 35 miles away. There was only one way to search systematically for fossils and that was to crawl along on the hands and knees, inspecting every inch of ground. Through such work, the Leakey collection of animal fossils and stone tools grew and grew. But 28 years went by with no sign of the men, or ape men, who manufactured the tools. It began to seem that the most primitive of hominids, the ape men, had lived at one place, South Africa, and that the most primitive stone tools had been made at another, East Africa. At least this was the baffling situation until July 17, 1959.

That morning Leakey awakened with a fever and headache. His wife insisted that he remain in camp. But their season was drawing to an end and the day could not be lost. Mary Leakey, accompanied by two of their Dalmatians, drove to the point where the party was working. As she crept along the hillside, a bit of bone lodged in a rockslide caught her eye. She recognized it as a piece of skull. She searched higher along the slope, and suddenly saw two big teeth, brown-black and almost iridescent, just eroding from the hill. She marked the spot with a small cairn of stone, ran to their Land Rover and sped back to camp.

Leakey heard the car racing up the road and sprang up in alarm, his first thought that his wife had been bitten by a snake that had slipped by the guard of the dogs. But as the car stopped he heard his wife shout, "I've got him! I've got him!" The "him," she felt sure, was man, the early man they had been seeking so many years. Leakey's fever and headache forgotten, they jumped in the car and sped down the trail as far as they could drive. The last half mile they covered at a run.

Mary Leakey's first impression had been right: the teeth were human or near-human. The two dropped to their hands and knees to examine them with the most minute care. Leakey could see that the dark molars glinting in the afternoon sun were twice as wide as the molars of modern man, but human in shape.

"I turned to look at Mary, and we almost cried with sheer joy, each seized by that terrific emotion that comes rarely in life," said Leakey. "After all our hoping and hardship and sacrifice at last we had reached our goal . . . we had discovered the world's earliest known human." The Leakeys went to work with camel's-hair brushes and dental picks. The palate to which the teeth were affixed came into view and then fragments of a skull. In order not to lose a single precious scrap they removed and sieved tons of scree, a fine rock debris, from the slope below the find. At the end of 19 days they had about 400 fragments.

While the delicate task of assembling the bits and pieces went on, the Leakeys continued to excavate the site. They had not only discovered the oldest near-man skull to be known in the whole of eastern and central Africa, but also a campsite of this ancient creature's. Scattered on what had been the shores of an ancient lake were nine pebble tools, not the most primitive Leakey had found at Olduvai, but very early ones. Lying about too were the fossil bones of animals the residents of the campsite had killed and eaten—rats, mice, frogs, lizards, birds, a snake, a tortoise, some young pigs, a juvenile giant ostrich. Nearly all these bones were broken, while the near-human skull and a tibia, a leg bone that also appeared in the stone of "Bed I" of the site were not. So ape man had killed the animals. But here were no giant beasts. Even with their pebble tools the beach dwellers evidently could not cope with the big animals of their day. Their prey were the young and the small.

The skull taking form from the fragments was that of an 18-year-old male. The unworn wisdom teeth and the fact that the suture joining the two halves of the skull had not yet closed indicated a young adult. In many ways the young male resembled the larger ape men of the south. In brain size and in general appearance he was at least a member of the australopithecine family. Yet as Leakey studied the skull more closely he saw significant differences. The face was not as apelike as that of the South Africans; the cheek had almost the curve of the human cheek. The palate was deeper and more modernly arched. The molars Mrs. Leakey had seen protruding from the hill were unusually large and heavy; they could have cracked nuts. But detailed study confirmed that they were like human teeth. Leakey made a bold decision to set up a new genus for this early Stone Age tool-user, and named him *Zinjanthropus boisei*. *Zinj* meant eastern Africa in Arabic; the *boisei* honored Charles Boise who had helped to finance the search for early man.

"Zinjanthropus, in spite of being classified in the sub-family *Australopithecinae* already exhibits specializations which foreshadow *Homo* . . ." wrote Leakey.

Bᴜᴛ how old was he? Luckily for science, not long after *Zinjanthropus* died a stream of lava poured in over the silt that covered him. Two scientists from the University of California, Jack Evernden and Garniss H. Curtis, extracted radioactive potassium from this volcanic cover and also from an older volcanic bed that underlay the *Zinj* site. By measuring the potassium's slow decay into argon they first fixed the startling age of about 1,750,000 years for *Zinj*. Later tests indicated that this might be at least half a million years too great; but in any event *Zinjanthropus* was of record-breaking age.

In the years while the Leakeys were probing Olduvai without finding man, they saw that the gorge nevertheless was virtually a book of life. In the five main deposits that cropped out in the 300-foot wall, there was a graduation of tools—from the chipped pebbles of Bed I at the bottom to the tools of contemporary men at the surface. There was a similar progression from the extinct animals at the bottom level to the animals of today roaming the Serengeti plains at the top. Among the pebble tools in the next-to-bottom bed Leakey found, early in his digging, some stone hand axes flaked on both sides.

They were known as Chellean hand axes, and there was nothing unique about their discovery. A century earlier similar axes had been found at Chelles-sur-Marne, a little east of Paris. Since then the same kind of axes had turned up in "digs" all over the world. They were found among the bones of giant animals—elephants, rhinoceroses and the like. But for all the thousands of Chellean axes uncovered at all the different sites, nobody had ever found Chellean man, the maker of the tools and the slayer of the big animals. Who he was and what he looked like remained one of the mysteries of archeology.

On December 1, 1960, Louis Leakey happened to take a backward glance along a slope where he was working in Olduvai's Bed II. From his vantage point he saw a small patch of deposits that had been overlooked. The afternoon light was failing, but first thing the next morning he went to investigate. "Imagine my joy when I walked into the tiny exposure and saw, sticking out of the bank, parts of a human skull," Leakey related. He soon freed the skull from its matrix—and there, to his even greater joy, was Chellean man! The vault of the skull was higher than in *Zinjanthropus* and the eyebrow ridges thrust out into an overhanging shelf.

"The new skull," Leakey reported, "is more or less the contemporary of Java Man and Peking Man and has certain very definite resemblances to these. . . . But it is much larger and differs from them in . . . significant characters."

All about the site lay Chellean tools. Like the earlier Oldowan chipped pebbles, they were made of oval or pear-shaped pieces of stone. But no longer did they have an untouched rounded end to fit into the palm of the hand. They were chipped all around the edges, first in one direction and then in the reverse, so that they had two faces and a zigzag or sinuous edge. With this potent implement, Chellean man could fashion spears to bring down and skin the largest of the animals. No longer was he limited to preying upon the young and small. Now he was a truly formidable hunter. The bones of the giant beasts he slew in many parts of the world testify to his new prowess.

Proconsul, *Australopithecus* (including *Zinjanthropus*), Chellean man—like the tools and animals, they succeeded one another in the deep African strata. Nowhere else in the world was there any other such progression or any other discovered evidence of man's earliest primate ancestors.

In 1952, even before the discovery of *Zinjanthropus* and Chellean man, the French paleontologist Père Pierre Teilhard de Chardin, speaking at the Wenner Gren Foundation's International Symposium on Anthropology at New York, had pointed to the full meaning of the African finds: "It becomes both difficult and unscientific not to accept the idea that the Dark Continent . . . acted as the main laboratory for the zoological development and the earliest establishment of man on this planet. It is apparently in the depths of Africa (and not on the shores of the Mediterranean Sea or on the Asiatic plateau), therefore, that the primeval center of human expansion and dispersion must have been located. . . ." By all indications man at last had found his birthplace—and his earliest ancestors. He was no longer a backgroundless, unrelated, unproved creature-from-nowhere on this planet.

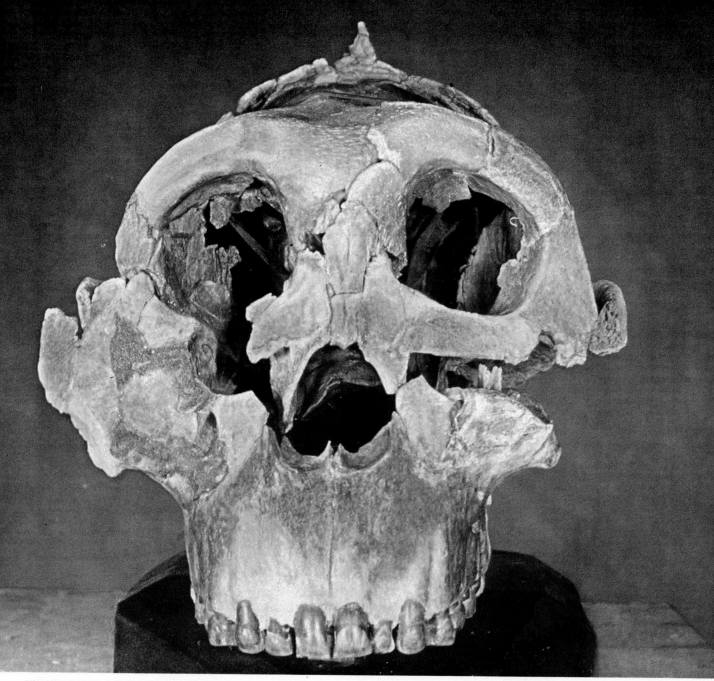

ZINJANTHROPUS, A TOOL-USING, VEGETARIAN AUSTRALOPITHECINE, LIVED ON TANGANYIKA'S SAVANNAS MORE THAN A MILLION YEARS AGO

The Ancestry of Man

Prehumans like Zinjanthropus (above) split off early from other primates. Early men prowled the prairies, while apes kept to the forests and monkeys to the trees. To survive on the plains, sub-humans turned apish play with sticks and stones into regular use of tools; arms made the man. Of many manlike species—some shown on the pages that follow—only one survived, Homo sapiens.

AFRICA'S 25-MILE-LONG OLDUVAI GORGE, A PART OF THE GREAT RIFT VALLEY, YIELDS REMAINS OF TWO DIFFERENT KINDS OF EARLY PRIMATES

SORTING FOSSILS, Dr. and Mrs. Leakey work in their tent at Olduvai. The gorge exposes living sites of one human type after another, heaped up in layers by lava flows and successive floods.

A Graveyard of Ancient Primates

No mammal fossils are harder to find than those of monkeys, apes and men. Primates generally live in forests and are too alert to be caught often in fossil-preserving lava flows, tar pits, quicksand, quagmires or flooding rivers. But over the past three decades one great treasury of human and subhuman relics has been uncovered: Olduvai Gorge in Tanganyika (*above*). It has been explored mainly by Dr. Louis S. B. Leakey and his wife Mary. Under their persevering scrabbling it has disgorged an amazing number of extinct giant mammals and hominids, including *Zinjanthropus* (*preceding page*) and an even earlier, meat-eating protoman who made tools and who may represent a transitional step toward the true *Homo* line. Radioactive dating indicates that the toolmaker lived about 1,750,000 years ago, which makes him the earliest "man" found to date.

CLAWING AT THE PAST, Dr. Leakey lies on his side in the hot Tanganyika sun to free an ancient bone. After a German butterfly hunter—who almost fell into the gorge in 1911—discovered that Olduvai is a fossil paradise, it lay unworked until 1931, when the Leakeys finally raised enough money to begin excavations. Their most important finds came after 20 years' digging.

A BABOON'S SKULL grins from limestone rock at Sterkfontein between the two wedges which will pry this fossil loose. A species now extinct, this animal was found along with several others, their heads crushed by crude stone weapons. And in this same rock, the weapons, too, were found: pebble tools employed by Australopithecines when they turned carnivorous.

SHAPED STONES from the Sterkfontein site near Pretoria show how the more intelligent and skillful Australopithecines began to make weapons. Between two lumps of quartzite, perhaps used as bludgeons, is a primitive hand ax with a crude cutting edge. None of these rocks is native to the excavation area, so it is assumed they were brought by early tool users.

The Critical Factor of Tools

Anthropologists acknowledge two critical turning points in the evolution of man: the first when his early mammalian ancestors got up and walked on their hind legs, thus making tool-using possible; and the second when, under the pressures of a drying climate, they shifted to a meat diet, thus making tool-using mandatory. For while a vegetarian could still pluck and dig for food with his bare hands, a meat eater had to invent substitutes for the fangs and claws he lacked to kill his prey.

Tools proved to be the crux of survival. Those who used them had to develop skills; eventually, when ordinary sticks and stones proved inadequate, they had to fabricate weapons, chipping and sharpening the rough stones, fashioning the sticks into spears. This put a premium on brain development, and in the meat-eating Australopithecine line, this was rapid, leading to an early toolmaker who shared the environment with *Paranthropus*. The latter, however, still a vegetarian, was eventually lost in an evolutionary backwater—though this and other early African hominids had learned to walk upright, they never learned to exploit fully the possibilities offered by their new way of life, and so, along with *Zinjanthropus*, they gradually became extinct.

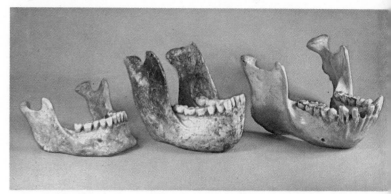

THREE JAWBONES show differences between an orangutan (*right*), *Paranthropus* and modern man (*left*). Massive teeth and jawbone structure are characteristics of the herbivores.

TWO SKULLS show how Australopithecines (*left*) began to evolve the rounded shape typical of man, whose lighter bones permitted the expansion of the brain demanded by tool-using.

157

PROCONSUL—or a creature much like him—was the common ancestor of men and apes. He prowled East Africa 20 to 25 million years ago. Hairy and slouching, he had less brain than a chimpanzee, but he was built to lead an agile life on or off the ground. He could have evolved either toward tree-living, like apes, or toward erect life on the grasslands, like early men.

From Apehood to Savagery

The earliest primates were small, stealthy night creatures of the trees, eating insects or whatever else they could lay hands on and surviving by their wits and adaptability. From them developed monkeys with fairly large brains and dexterous hands; they could pick things up, examine them and presumably think about them. Over 10 million years ago a versatile monkey of the Proconsul type *(opposite)* sired two distinct lines: the forest apes and prairie-prowling, cave-camping prehumans such as *Australopithecus (right)*. One of many branches of the australopithecines survived to become true men like Peking man below, a probable precursor of modern Orientals.

AUSTRALOPITHECUS, an ape man of about one million years ago, walked erect *(right)*, used his arms and hands to make simple pebble tools, and possibly mastered a few speech sounds.

PEKING MAN left his remains about 360,000 years ago in fossil-famous Choukoutien cave in Northern China. There he lit fires, killed deer, flaked out stone tools and probably talked. His own bones—not gnawed but split open—indicate that he also practiced cannibalism. He and the other early primates on these and the following four pages were painted by Maurice Wilson.

159

SWANSCOMBE MAN, who hunted now-extinct deer along the brooks of the English countryside of 250,000 B.C., may have been the first example of *Homo sapiens*, the present human species. He had thicker bones than man today, but no other essential differences so far as is known. In this painting, Swanscombe hunters come in for the kill wielding their wooden spears.

Flint hand axes lie discarded on the ground around the horned remains of earlier kills. The tusk sinking into the sand at center belonged to an elephant like those seen parading past on the riverbank in the distance. The skull in the foreground belonged to a huge ice-age ox, the aurochs, which is an ancestor of modern cattle. An aurochs bull stood six feet high at the shoulder.

NEANDERTHALS, a rugged early human breed, roamed Europe and the Middle East about 75,000 years ago. They may have interbred with early *Homo sapiens*, who was their contemporary, competitor and possibly their exterminator. This family is enjoying a moment of comparative peace and safety in an open space before its cave home at the foot of the Rock of Gibraltar.

At that time, much of the earth's water was tied up in ice-caps and the lowered oceans left many sea caves high and dry. The Neanderthal father is trying on one deerskin cape while the mother dresses another—and the children quarrel. The dead birds at left are a great auk—an extinct, flightless, penguin-sized diving bird—and an alpine chough, a relative of the crow.

CRO-MAGNONS, the Neanderthals' survivors and successors, hunted in Europe during the late ice ages and immortalized their prowess in many cave paintings. They were big, essentially modern Caucasoids who wore sewn clothes of hide and fur, wielded spear throwers and antler-tipped spears, and differed little from barbarian tribesmen of Julius Caesar's day. On this warm spring day three warriors march into camp, hot from the hunt, half-stripped and laden with game. The veteran at left carries an alpine antelope, or chamois, the younger man at right an arctic fox. Beside the fire, fish are being smoked from a pole. Below at left lies one horn of a saiga antelope. The rocky overhang at the right serves as the hunters' temporary shelter.

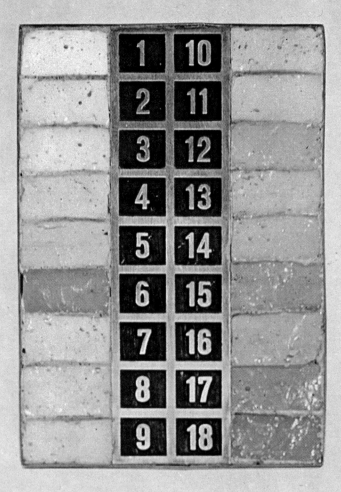

HUMAN SKIN ranges in color from almost pure white to jet-black, as shown on these ceramic tiles of the Von Luschan scale. Each variation is caused by a special combination of the genes which affect skin color.

8

The Emergence of Homo Sapiens

A MILLION years or so ago, some of those near-men of South Africa—who may or may not have been among our direct ancestors—took to globe-trotting. The world beckoned them; perhaps the game always looked to be a little more plentiful a little farther on, and in their time "farther on" was uniquely reachable. The wide continental ice sheets had crept down from the north, and as vast quantities of water were locked up in the miles-deep ice, the sea level receded. All through the world the shores widened and land bridges were revealed, wide and crossable, between some of the earth's major land masses.

So early man pushed on, dry-shod, out of Africa into southern and western Europe, where some of his primitive stone tools have been found; into India south of the Himalayas, where he left more of his enduring flints to mark his passing; and along a warm, dry corridor into a southern extension of the Asiatic continent that is now the island of Java. There the skull and leg bones of *Pithecanthropus* testified to his arrival and survival. Probably a little later the migrators turned north into China.

By the time these pioneering primates reached Java, their brain capacity had increased from the 450 to 650 cubic centimeters of their forebears to about 900;

EVOLUTIONARY CHANGES IN ANIMAL BRAINS

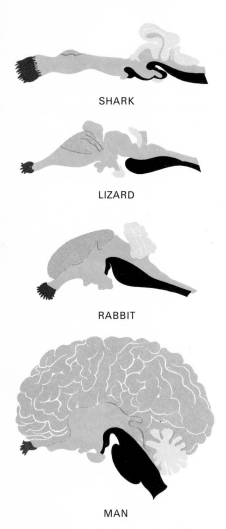

SHARK

LIZARD

RABBIT

MAN

Different parts of the brain control different functions. Among lower orders, like sharks, the inner brain (red), cerebellum (pink), medulla (black) and frontal lobe (dark gray), which control coordination plus automatic activities of the body and personality, dominate the brain area. Only a small portion is given to the cerebrum (light gray), or thinking apparatus. However, as animals ascend the evolutionary scale, thinking becomes more crucial to survival and the cerebrum grows larger and more convoluted, and areas governing instinct become proportionately smaller.

and by the time of their establishment at Choukoutien in China, brain capacity was up to about 1,100 cubic centimeters. It is likely that those with the larger brains had the best chance of surviving to reproduce themselves among the perils of new lands, and of finding ways to adapt to new modes of living. The selective pressures for better brains must have been very intense. Their locomotor skeleton, while it remained essentially that of the earlier australopithecines, was already human.

While Java man and Peking man flourished in the Far East, other and similar early men from central Africa were getting established in Europe and northwest Africa, though there is only scant evidence of their presence. In all of Europe only two skulls, one of them half-preserved, show that they were there and tell of what they were. In North Africa so far, only fragmentary jaws and teeth go back to the Middle Pleistocene epoch, a time now roughly and uncertainly estimated at some 500,000 to 150,000 years ago. The anthropoids' family tree branched out richly in the Pleistocene, and until much more evidence is dug up, the question of exactly who begat whom among all the possible predecessors of modern man is highly debatable.

THOUGH the provable record of man and near-man is still obscure through the long middle period of the last million years, the geologic record is generally explicit and clear. Three more times the ice thrust down from the north, covering much of Europe, Asia and North America with a solid icecap much like that which mantles Greenland today. It is certain that each time the cold and ice advanced, man was driven back south. Between the glaciations the climate waxed warmer and more hospitable and man moved north again, finding rich hunting in the wake of the receding ice. Late in the Pleistocene a group of men distinctly different from all the more primitive types whose traces have so far been discovered gradually became predominant in Europe and western Asia. The bones of more than 100 of them have been found in places ranging from southwest France and Gibraltar to Italy, Germany, Yugoslavia, southern Russia, Iraq, Iran and Palestine.

These were the Neanderthals, so called for the first of their kind, found in the Neander valley in Germany. They averaged five foot five in height and were ruggedly built. As we have seen, their brains, lodged in massive heads, were in the upper size range of modern human brains. They made skillfully chipped stone tools and with them hunted a wide range of game, even bringing down such massive animals as the mammoth and woolly rhinoceros. Without doubt they were men of dawning religious feeling—men who could *reflect*—for the arrangement of some of their bones bespeaks a ceremonial burial. In one Swiss cave they left the skulls of bears in the elevated dignity of objects of worship, in what appears to have been a shrine.

In Neanderthal man's case, the relative abundance of fossil material has produced confusion instead of clarity; there are almost as many theories of his history, dispersal and mysterious fate as there are skulls or scholars. After extended study of the whole group, F. Clark Howell of the University of Chicago was convinced, however, that "a single, variable, racial group seems to have been everywhere present in Europe." The coming of the last ice age, it is believed, disrupted this continuity. As the cold increased and the Scandinavian ice sheet again edged southward, the glaciers that filled the mountain valleys grew far out across the plains. The ice drove a wide and impassable barrier between the Neanderthals of western and southern Europe and those of eastern

Europe and the Middle East. Gene interchange was barred as effectively as if the colonies had been isolated on widely separated islands.

Thus imprisoned by the ice and the sea, the western Neanderthals developed in their own distinctive way. They could not get out, and no new racial stocks could get in to interbreed with them. The concentration of one genetic pattern, many anthropologists believe, caused the westerners to become more Neanderthalian, with heavier eyebrow ridges and more massive jaws. Conditions were different for the Neanderthals in eastern Europe and the Middle East. There the glaciers lay far to the north or were localized in the Balkan and Carpathian Mountains. The wide, flat steppes and high plateaus supported large herds of animals, and roots and berries grew in the wooded valleys. Bands of men could move about freely, and there was nothing to hinder a free genetic interchange over this whole area—the regions bordering the Black Sea and southwestern Asia. Neanderthal-like people wandered as far east as Samarkand and as far south as Haifa.

Some of the Neanderthals lived in hillside caves looking out on the Mediterranean, and others in the caves bordering the "fertile crescent" of the Tigris and Euphrates Rivers. One such cave, in a rocky slope of the Zagros Mountains, about 250 miles north of Baghdad, turned its arched mouth to the south. In winter the sun shone warm and bright on part of its floor, and the chilly winds whistled by. In 1951 when Ralph S. Solecki, an anthropologist at Columbia University, first saw Shanidar Cave, Kurdish goatherds and their animals were living in small brush huts and corrals on its capacious floor. Undoubtedly their forefathers had lived there in much the same way. Solecki thought that the cave would be a promising place to search for early man.

In three seasons of work, an expedition sent a shaft through 45 feet of floor deposits before bedrock was reached. The thick load of fallen rocks and earth had accumulated over a period of about 100,000 years.

In Layer D, 16 feet below the surface and extending down to bedrock, lay the skeletons of seven Neanderthals, one of them an infant. Several had been killed by rocks falling from the cave ceiling. In many ways these people of Shanidar resembled the early Neanderthal men of Europe—there was the massive jaw, the sloping forehead and the bulging brow ridge. Solecki reported that there were "few suggestions of progress toward the features of *Homo sapiens*," modern man. In one case, the brow ridge was not a continuous one running across the forehead. It had a depression between the eyes, as does the forehead of contemporary man. In other caves in the Middle East were other remains with a curious mixture of Neanderthal and modern features. Those from Palestine most nearly resembled modern human skeletons.

Had a different, more modern people moved into this eastern area, or was the change a result of the evolution of the people there? As yet there is no answer, but Howell suggests: "It is difficult to escape the conclusion, although there is still inadequate evidence to fix exactly the region and time, that the southwest Asian area, and including Southern Russia, was a primary one in the evolutionary transformation of protosapiens people, who had some general early Neanderthal affinities, into anatomically modern man. . . ." Only in this area, Howell argues, was there an appropriate base for the rise of the modern men who were soon to take over the earth.

Though the full story of the Neanderthals is hazy and uncertain, even deeper mystery surrounds their disappearance. After thriving some 75,000 to 50,000

LAND BRIDGES OF THE PAST AND THE PRESENT

GREATER EUROPE

If the water around Europe were lowered 300 feet, the pink areas on the map would emerge as land, permitting passage of animals. Such a shift in sea level during the ice ages is believed to have linked Britain to Europe, Spain and Italy to Africa.

THE ISTHMUS OF PANAMA

A bridge now exists between North and South America, but for long periods during the past, Central America was nothing but a series of islands (pink areas). The present bridge arose from the oceans between two and three million years ago.

years ago, while the northern part of the Eurasian continent still was ice-covered and bleak, the Neanderthals vanished. In the caves of East and West their tools, the bones of the animals they killed and their own sturdy bones come to an abrupt end. At Shanidar Cave the end comes in deposits 29 feet above bedrock. Higher levels contain only the tools and remains of another kind of man. In some caves a "sterile" layer, one without bones or tools and indicating an accumulation during years of severe cold or flooding, comes briefly between.

What brought about the demise, if it was a demise, of the men who had earlier spread with such hardihood over a large section of the earth? Carleton S. Coon, professor of anthropology at the University of Pennsylvania, and himself the excavator of seven of the caves in which early man lived, suggests that wet, bitter cold may largely have wiped out Neanderthal man. Earlier peaks of cold had been dry and easier to survive. There is some belief that Neanderthal lost out to newer, abler hunters in the competition for game, also that he was killed off by newcomers, much as were the aborigines of Australia and the American Indians.

In the caves, the remains of *Homo sapiens* nearly always lie immediately above those of Neanderthal man; there is almost no intermingling. A few small fragments of bone have cast some doubt, however, upon this abrupt succession and suggest that the first of the modern men may have appeared in Europe 250,000 or more years ago, even before the Neanderthals held sway. A nearly complete skull was found at Steinheim, near Stuttgart, in 1933. Two years later some skull fragments were found deep in very old gravels on the banks of the Thames River at Swanscombe, not far from London. The three bones from Swanscombe have a *sapiens* conformation which impresses many authorities. If Swanscombe man lived at the time gravels were laid down by the river, he would be about 250,000 years old; and if he is indeed a modern man, then his kind, *Homo sapiens*, would be far older than the cave deposits have indicated. Other fragments that indicate an earlier appearance for him are an incomplete skullcap and a *sapiens*-appearing piece of frontal bone discovered in the grotto of Fontéchevade, in southwest France. Associated with them are the bones of animals which lived before the last ice age.

But the question is not settled. Until more complete material is available, at least one scientific journal has urged anthropologists to withhold judgment and avoid basing broad and far-reaching theories of evolution on such fragmentary materials as those found at Swanscombe and Fontéchevade. There is no doubt, however, that a modern, European form of *Homo sapiens* and his different way of life had replaced Neanderthal man by 40,000 years ago, and perhaps by 50,000. At this point the record becomes full and easy of interpretation.

The green valleys in the beautiful Dordogne region of France are walled in by gentle limestone cliffs, which at many points are honeycombed with caves, many of them the longtime homes of Neanderthal man. Sometime after he disappeared from these caves, modern *Homo sapiens* moved in. From the cave ledges he could safely survey the whole valley for game or enemies. To this day, people still build their homes against the sheltering cliffs and use the rock face for a rear wall, or the caves themselves for rear rooms.

The men who took over in the Dordogne, and who quickly occupied many other parts of Europe and the Near East, were somewhat taller than those Neanderthals whose stature is known. Their skulls were thinner and higher, their foreheads nearly vertical, their features finer, their mouths retracted, and their posture and carriage as upright as anyone's. They were Cro-Magnon men, named for the cave near the little riverside village of Les Eyzies where their traces were first discovered.

Though their brains were no larger than those of Neanderthal men, these new men put their brains to new uses. They made a wide variety of greatly improved tools. They knew how to select a sizable piece of flint, shape it into cylindrical form and with one skillful blow knock off a long flake blade, in effect a long knife with two razor edges coming together in a point. By applying pressure to the cylinder with another piece of stone or bone, they removed additional chips exactly as they wanted. The cylinder was portable and a new tool could be made on the hunt if an old one broke. With this new arsenal—quite advanced over any ever made by Neanderthal man—the largest of animals could be brought down with a new efficiency, and their skins turned into warm clothing. Hundreds of awls and needles used in the making of clothing were found in the caves.

I N some of the cave passages running back into the cliffs, these mighty hunters began to scratch the outlines of the animals they pursued: mammoths, horses, bison, wild oxen and rhinoceroses as well as their favorite, reindeer. Often they selected a rounded place in the rock to give a sculptured effect to their art, for it was art. Soon they were outlining the animals in black on the stone walls of the caves, and in time they began to paint in earth colors. At Lascaux in the main cave and several adjoining galleries, nearly 500 bulls, horses, antelopes and even a herd of reindeer swimming a river are painted with an artistry, power and accuracy of movement that have not been surpassed. The paintings there must be considered one of the world's great assemblages of art. By their art these men of the caves, the Cro-Magnons, proved their possession of the highest capacities yet achieved in the long course of evolution. Their cultural objects proved their status without question and abundantly. And as reflective beings they had come a long, long way: many of their caves were used only as places of ritual worship, and they supported some of their fellows as full-time artists.

These new men—*Homo sapiens* like ourselves—may have arisen in one locality and spread over the globe. Or, by another theory, several subspecies in different parts of the world may independently have progressed to *Homo sapiens* status, and gone on to develop as the present races of man. Whatever their birthplace or places, the new men absorbed or extinguished all others who had come before them. Modern men of the Mongoloid race, for example, moved along the eastern edge of Asia and up to the Bering Strait, where they crossed the land bridge into Alaska. In the New World they worked their way down the west coast and to the very tip of the southern continent. In Europe as the ice began its latest retreat, some 12,000 years ago, men pushed on into the thawing north. The only lands these new men failed to occupy were the bleak tundra of Canada, the forbidding shores of Greenland, the oceanic islands and Antarctica.

Even at the time of their earliest known appearance, these men who were inheriting the earth were biologically as advanced as any men who have been born since. In brain size, in posture and in physical organization, the three billion human beings who are their descendants of today have not basically changed the patterns that evolution had already built into their bodies.

Not that the human body is unimprovable. But what has won man his dominion over the earth has not been his physique but his discovery and exploitation of a new kind of evolution. For more than half a billion years life evolved solely through mutation, through the sexual recombination of genes and through natural selection. But man—haltingly at first, then with an accelerating rush

ASIA AND NORTH AMERICA

The similarity of fossil and living animals and plants in Asia and the Americas suggests the presence of an ancient bridge across the Bering Strait. It is believed that the first men to inhabit the North American continent came over it from Siberia.

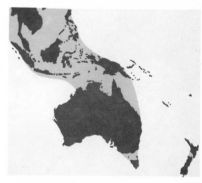

SOUTHEAST ASIA AND AUSTRALIA

The oldest bridge of all, and probably the first to disappear, was one that connected Australia with Southeast Asia. It vanished even before the advent of placental mammals, leaving Australia with more primitive types which still persist today.

over the past few thousand years—began adapting the environment to fit himself. He created a nongenetic system of inheritance and evolution, the transmission of information and tradition through what is broadly called culture. Genetic evolution has never before been relegated to a minor role by any species, and in its ultimate importance man's assumption of control over his own evolution is probably secondary only to the origination of life itself.

In adapting the conditions of life to suit his own requirements, man not only reshaped the existing environments in which he found himself; he also invented entirely new environments. Within them he brought warmth and cold, among many other factors, under his control and, to a great extent, flood and drought. By an increasingly complex system of food production and distribution, he offset the universal danger of starvation; and by harnessing energy sources greater than his own muscle power, he freed his species from limitations of time and space. And while the whole ramified civilizing process introduced many new hazards to survival, it wiped out or drastically reduced many old ones.

THE results are everywhere apparent as man, the first and only creature to be *aware* of his own evolving, also begins to be aware of some of the incredibly complicated implications of what he has wrought. For example, millions of human beings who would have died if natural selection had gone on operating without artificial restriction have survived to reproduce their kind. The general flouting of the process of natural (biological) selection has also begun to affect the human genetic pool, the total hereditary material, or DNA reservoir, of the race, for mutation still goes on apace. As it has always been since life began, some of the DNA of man and all other living things continues to be struck by radiation or altered by other agents; and most mutations, it has long been known, are injurious. In the past, natural selection efficiently eliminated the more injurious ones; the mutant individuals simply died before producing offspring. This is no longer quite true of man.

Geneticists estimate that about one sex cell in every 50,000 produced by a normal person carries a mutant gene causing a cancer of the eye called retinoblastoma. It appears in childhood. If it is not treated, as it could not be in the past, few of its victims live long enough to produce children, and the disastrous mutant gene thus had been thwarted from seriously affecting the population. However, if retinoblastoma is treated with the best of modern medical skill, about 70 per cent of the afflicted children can be saved. They are then free to pass along their harmful inheritance to their children, who in turn, assuming they survive, are free to do likewise. Any such mutant gene frequency thus can increase enormously beyond its "normal" rate of appearance—and geneticists can only speculate on how the rate itself may be raised by widespread exposure to increased radiation, to pesticides and to other new man-made mutagens.

New drugs and a generally improved environment now save the lives of thousands of people whose genetic make-up renders them susceptible to tuberculosis. In Darwin's time this infectious disease annually killed 500 people out of every 100,000 in industrial areas; today the death rate from tuberculosis in America is only 6.5 per 100,000. Many who now live, instead of dying from the disease, of course pass along their susceptibility to their children. Will it be offset in future generations by other genes inherited from nonsusceptible parents? Or will the detrimental genes accumulate, to build a higher susceptibility in the future? And in either event, if the generations of tuberculosis-susceptibles can live normal lives without ever actually acquiring the disease, who is to say they should not live and reproduce, or that their gene variation really matters? Geneticists are not the only ones bothered by such questions.

At least, though, while the indiscriminate saving of lives represents one of the highest and proudest achievements of cultural evolution, the geneticists urge that its genetic consequences to the human race be looked at. As Hermann J. Muller, one of the world's leading authorities on mutation, points out: "The saving of lives for reproduction by ever more efficient medical and other technical and sociological aids inevitably results in an increasing accumulation of randomly occurring detrimental mutations. These must adversely affect health, intellect, powers of appreciation and expression, and the genetic basis even of our co-operative disposition itself." To the question whether man is not frustrating natural selection and polluting his own gene pool, Theodosius Dobzhansky reflects that "if our culture has an ideal, it is the sacredness of human life. A society that refused, on eugenic grounds, to cure children of retinoblastoma would, in our eyes, lose more by moral degradation than it gained genetically. Not so easy, however, is the question whether a person who knows he carries the gene for retinoblastoma, or a similarly deleterious gene, has a right to have children. . . . It may well be that the social cost of maintaining some genetic variants will be so great that artificial selection against them will be ethically, as well as economically, the most acceptable and wisest solution."

Many people, including some geneticists, suspect that human interference with natural selection is also favoring the increase of the less intelligent. Some inconclusive studies have indicated that parents scoring low on intelligence tests tend to produce more children than those making high scores. Certainly, says the British biologist Peter Brian Medawar in *The Future of Man*, "Profound changes in habits of fertility have been taking place over the past 50 or 100 years; and they are not yet complete. The decline of intelligence (if indeed it is declining) may be a purely temporary phenomenon. . . . But even if the decline looked as if it might be long lasting, it would not be irremediable. Changes in the structure of taxation and in the award of family allowances and educational grants may already have removed some of the factors which have discouraged the more intelligent from having larger families; and in 25 years' time we may be laughing at our present misgivings. I do not, however, think that there is anything very much to be amused about just at present."

Even setting aside the so-far-unsubstantiated fear that humanity is now genetically discriminating against its own intelligence, some leading men in the evolutionary field are apprehensive about the direction in which modern scientific and social advances are carrying man and his gene pool. Muller has called the present trends "a kind of natural selection in reverse." Bernhard Rensch, a German authority on comparative zoology, has warned that "the steady mutations that produce mainly bad characters will cause a regressive development. I believe that it is the duty of biologists to discuss the problem of the human future, even if this is not an exact science but only speculation."

In lectures, in scientific papers and in books the scientific debate goes on, not always in the restrained language of science. The subject is of profound importance, being nothing less than the future of man and his planet, and it is rendered more urgent by the fact that man for the first time has the power to control that future or to obliterate it.

Despite the grave dangers, and no scientist minimizes them, many participants in the great discussion believe that man may be able to direct his own

INHERITED CHARACTERS OF THE FACE AND HEAD

Inherited characters are governed by an interplay of dominant and recessive genes. This table shows which features of the human face and head are dominant (D) and which are recessive (R).

Roman nose (D)
Concave nose (R)
Straight-tip nose (D)
Turned-up nose (R)
Wide nostrils (D)
Narrow nostrils (R)
Full lips (D)
Thin lips (R)
Dimpled chin (D)
Nondimpled chin (R)
Clockwise hair whorl (D)
Counterclockwise hair whorl (R)
Dark hair (D)
Light hair color (R)
Baldness in men (D)
Baldness in women (R)
Free ear lobes (D)
Attached ear lobes (R)
Dark eye color (D)
Light eye color (R)
White blaze in hair (D)
Red hair (R)
Prematurely gray hair (D)
Body hairlessness (R)
Widow's peak (D)
Freckles (D)
Excessively pointed ears (D)
Drooping eyelids (ptosis) (D)
Ability to roll tongue (D)

evolution without wrecking it. "He should be able to replace the blind force of natural selection by conscious direction, based on his knowledge of nature and on his values," says Dobzhansky. "It is as certain that such direction will be needed as it is questionable whether man is ready to provide it."

Muller puts it more optimistically: "We have at least glimpsed the grand panorama of . . . evolution in the past, and so we know of what seeming miracles the plasticity of protoplasm—or DNA, if you like—is ultimately capable. It is true that with our present genetic basis, culture alone has carried us very far and can carry us very much farther, and, wisely developed, can give every man a fitting place under the sun.

"It is also true that, even with human aid, biological progress is far slower than that of culture. But the total advance is not the sum of these two; it is more like the product or even the exponent. Even as our own culture could not mean very much to the most superior ape, the culture of a mere million years from now will be so rich and advanced in its potentialities of experience and accomplishment that in it we, with our genetic constitution of today, would be like imbeciles in the palace. And so I believe that not only our cultural, but also our biological evolution will go on now to undreamed-of heights."

THE late Père Pierre Teilhard de Chardin was a philosopher among paleontologists and an unorthodox thinker who was somewhat ahead of his time and his church as well. In his writings he was consummately hopeful about where human evolution was heading: it was bound for an "Omega point" where the conscience and the consciousness of all mankind would unite to work for good, and for God. "Man is not the center of the universe as once we thought in our simplicity," he declared, "but something much more wonderful—the arrow pointing the way to the final unification of the world in terms of life. Man alone constitutes the last-born, the freshest, the most complicated, the most subtle of all the successive layers of life. . . ."

"Without going beyond the limits of scientific probability," wrote Père Teilhard in *The Phenomenon of Man*, "we can say that life still has before it long periods of geological time in which to develop. Moreover, in its thinking form, it still shows every sign of energy in full expansion. On the one hand, compared with the zoological layers which preceded it . . . mankind is so young that it could almost be called new-born. On the other hand, to judge from the rapid developments of thought in the short period of a few dozen centuries, this youth bears within it the indications and the promises of an entirely new biological cycle. Thus in all probability, between our modern earth and the ultimate earth, there stretches an immense period, characterized not by a slowing-down but by a speeding-up and by the definitive florescence of the forces of evolution along the line of the human shoot."

Something around two billion years saw the evolution of life. Possibly two million years have seen the evolution of ape man into the genus *Homo*. A single century has brought an understanding of the evolutionary forces shaping life. A few decades have unearthed the fossils, the tools and the related evidence to demonstrate the actual events in the evolution of man and of life in general. An even fewer years have revealed the base of it all, the miracle molecules of DNA. Only today is man recognizing that as he reshapes his world and replaces the relentless but stabilizing action of physical selection with a new, cultural evolution and inheritance, he is taking control of the future. Therein lies the climax of all the eons, the epochs and the years.

MONGOLOID

NEGROID

CAUCASOID

AUSTRALOID

CAPOID

ALL OF THE WORLD'S THREE BILLION HUMAN BEINGS ARE DESCENDED FROM ONE OR MORE OF THESE FIVE BASIC RACIAL TYPES OF MANKIND

Man and His Genes

Man's striking diversity of racial forms depends on the combined action of tiny genetic differences. In these combinations each single gene subtly affects one or more characters, their interaction resulting in a harmonious system. Many genetic variations have been helpful to man and are now part of his legacy; other dangerous ones may create lethal handicaps whenever they arise.

ETHIOPIAN

ARAB

AINU

VIETNAMESE

NAVAHO INDIAN

FORMOSAN

POLYNESIAN

MELANESIAN

PAPUAN

The Many Faces of Man

People today like to emphasize the oneness of man as though no racial divisions really existed. In actual fact, man is united in one species, but is racially divided into more than 30 subgroupings which are distinct from each other in genetic type and in details of physical appearance. A few of these subdivisions of man are pictured above. Naturally individuals differ within groups, but what sets a group apart is

VEDDA

BERBER

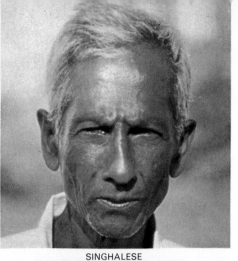

SINGHALESE

SIBERIAN

MONGOLIAN

KOREAN

PYGMY

NEGRITO

HOTTENTOT

that the majority inherit genetic characteristics peculiar to the group.

Man has come by his kaleidoscopic changes partly by being a wanderer. Over the past 150,000 years, as he searched for new hunting grounds, he spread into almost every region of the globe and, by natural selection, gradually built up the traits that adapted him best to a variety of environments. Thus, the wide, flat nose and folded eyelids of the Mongolian are adaptive for the rigors of the northern Asiatic cold. Similarly, the dark skin of the Negro protects him from overdoses of penetrating rays from the strong tropical sun. Genetic traits which are not helpful, or in some cases positively harmful, tend to be selected against, although they keep cropping up, as the examples on the following pages show.

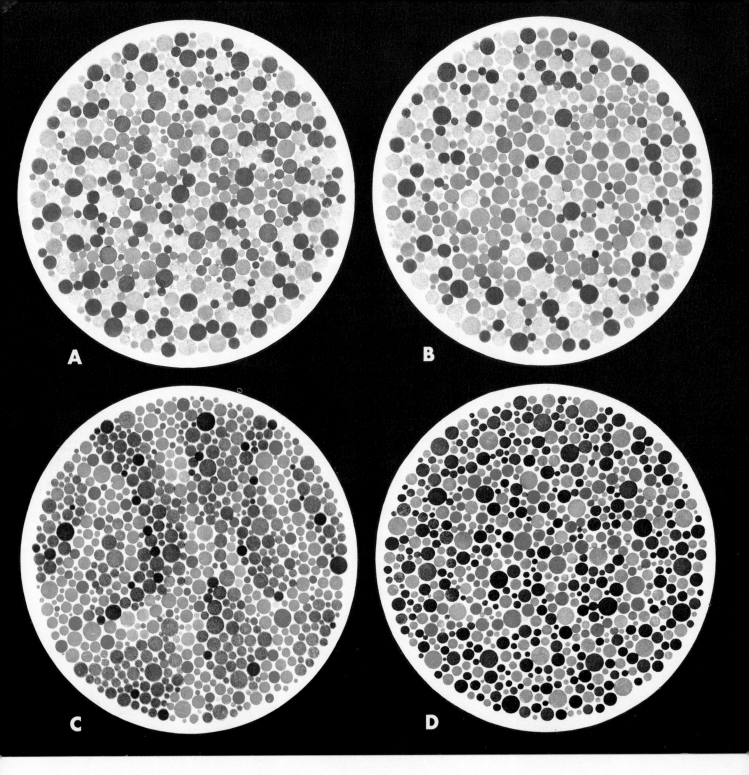

Recessive Traits: Some Bad, Some Worse

Along with the genes which all members of a race have in common, there are rare genes, some lethal, some beneficial, some inconsequential, which can crop up in individuals of all races. A few of these genetic odds and ends are shown here and on the following pages.

The traits of hemophilia *(opposite)* and of color blindness *(above)*, for example, are not only caused by recessive genes, but they are also confined almost exclusively to men. A woman may have a single hemophilia gene and will not suffer from the disease, but if she confers that one gene on a son, he will. The chance of the boy living long enough to marry another carrier is quite remote, and it explains why there are so very few female hemophiliacs—one in many million girls as against one in 10,000 boys.

COLOR BLINDNESS prevents distinguishing one light wavelength from another—seeing colors. The chart opposite is a test for color blindness. If you are not color-blind at all, you see a 29 in cut A, 45 in B, nothing in C and 26 in D. If you are red-blind, you see only the 6 in D; if green-blind, only the 2. If you can see neither green nor red, you will see a 70 in A, a 5 in C and nothing in B or D. No figures show to the totally color-blind.

HEMOPHILIA, an hereditary defect of the blood, was passed on to many of Europe's ruling families by Queen Victoria, shown presiding over an 1884 gathering in Coburg (*right*). Seventeen of the people in this group were her descendants (*in italic type in key*). Two days before, they had watched the marriage of two of her grandchildren, and the one next to wed was Alexandra of Hesse (21)—to Russia's last Czar (20). Four of Victoria's children (*chart below*) had hemophilia: Leopold and three daughters, who were all carriers. The disease slows blood-clotting time; its victims may bleed to death from small cuts. Women pass it on, but rarely suffer from it themselves.

1 Prince Louis of Battenberg	11 Princess Philip of Saxe-Coburg	21 *Princess Alexandra of Hesse*
2 Grand Duke Paul of Russia	12 Grand Duke Vladimir of Russia	22 *Princess Louis of Battenberg*
3 Prince Ferdinand of Romania	13 *Duke of Connaught*	23 *Princess Henry of Prussia*
4 Count Mensdorff	14 *Prince of Wales*	24 Grand Duchess Vladimir of Russia
5 Grand Duke Serge of Russia	15 *Princess Henry of Battenberg*	25 *Duchess of Saxe-Coburg-Gotha*
6 *Princess Ferdinand of Romania*	16 *Princess Alexandra of Saxe-Coburg-Gotha*	26 *Kaiser Wilhelm II*
7 *Prince Henry of Prussia*	17 *Hereditary Princess of Saxe-Meiningen*	27 Queen Victoria
8 Grand Duchess Serge of Russia	18 Duchess of Connaught	28 *Empress Frederick of Germany*
9 Duke of Saxe-Coburg-Gotha	19 *Prince Alfred of Saxe-Coburg-Gotha*	29 *Princess Beatrice of Saxe-Coburg-Gotha*
10 Prince Henry of Battenberg	20 Cesarevitch	30 *Princess Feodore of Saxe-Meiningen*

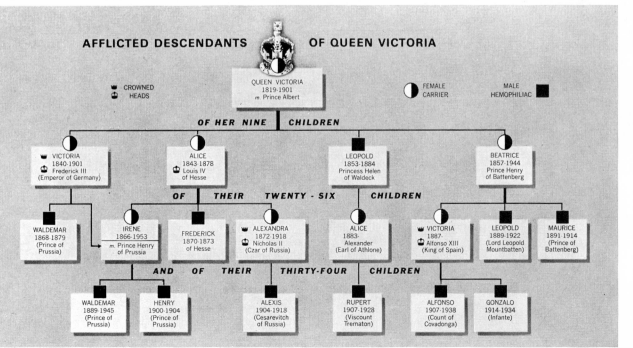

THE LONG PERSISTENCE
OF A ROYAL TRAIT

The Hapsburg lip, a curious pouting idiosyncrasy in which the lower lip and usually the lower jaw protrude, sometimes forcing the mouth partly open, has appeared in generation after generation of this famous European ruling family. Here in contemporary portraits we see five instances of the lip, unchanged over a spread of 388 years. Considered an excellent example of the long persistence of dominant genes, this oddity has also shown up in the faces of some Hapsburg women. One of them was Maria Teresa, Queen of Hungary and Bohemia in the 18th Century.

KAISER MAXIMILIAN I

EMPEROR CHARLES V

AN ALBINO MELANESIAN sits among dark fellow tribesmen at a Trobriand Island feast. He is genetically unable to produce melanin, the protective pigment that colors skin, eyes and hair.

Some Trade-Marks of Heredity

Anyone able to roll his tongue like the young woman opposite usually takes this fact for granted. It seems like a commonplace trick. Yet there are many people who cannot do it. This is because tongue-rolling is an inherited trait specifically determined by a single dominant gene, one of many that give us unusual characteristics. A Roman nose, the absence of a sense of smell, right-handedness, prematurely gray hair, absence of thumbnails and astigmatism are all apparently dominant traits handed down to us from parents or grandparents. Sometimes the trait is so clear and individualistic that the handing-down process can be traced back many generations. In the case of the Hapsburg family, an old line of European royalty, a peculiar protrusion of the lower lip has appeared in dozens of individuals since at least the 15th Century.

Fortunately, most dominant traits, which recur so frequently, are harmless. A harmful characteristic tends to be recessive, which means there is much less chance of it appearing. An example is albinism, arising from the body's inability to produce protective melanin pigment. Only one in thousands of Caucasoid babies is born an albino—as against one in perhaps half a dozen born with the related but dominant tendency to freckle (*opposite*). In an albino, the hair is white, the eyes red (they lack the pigment that normally masks their tiny blood vessels) and the skin so fair that even light exposure to the sun will cause terrible sunburn.

ARCHDUKE FERDINAND

PHILIP IV OF SPAIN

ARCHDUKE CHARLES OF TESCHEN

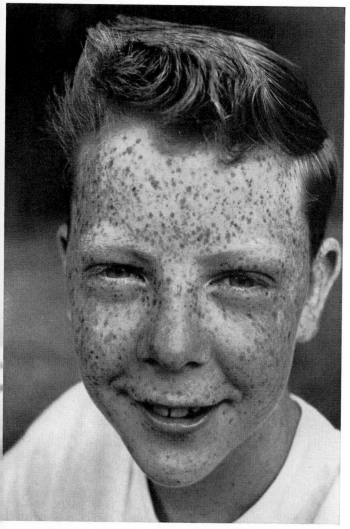

A PIEBALD SUNTAN is what this youngster's freckles really are. A dominant gene causes his skin to produce an uneven pattern of protective melanin pigment when it is exposed to the sun.

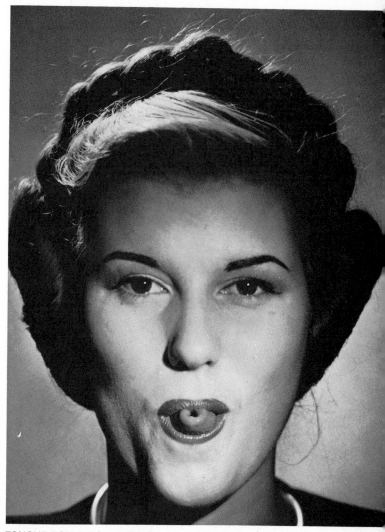

TONGUE-ROLLING is possible for seven of 10 people who have a certain dominant gene. Fewer than one in 1,000 can roll the tongue the other way, folding the tip back into the mouth.

PLAYING UNCONCERNEDLY, Willie Bee Johnson might be any normal American Negro boy. On each hand, however, he has six fingers, on each foot, six toes, marking him the victim of a rare dominant gene. Luckily, polydactyly does not interfere with normal functioning. Running strongly in the Johnson family, it at one time gave 10 living members 18 extra fingers and toes.

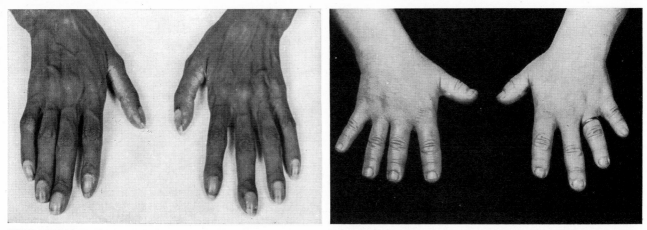

CONTRASTING EFFECTS OF TWO DOMINANT GENES ARE SPIDER-FINGEREDNESS (LEFT) AND STUNTED FINGERS CAUSED BY BRACHYPHALANGY

Variations in the Extremities

An enormous genetic variability among humans is found in their extremities—their hands, feet and ears. This is natural, since small modifications in the shape of an ear lobe or the length of a finger are not critical to survival. However, serious deformities like clubfeet or toelessness also appear, but more rarely since their possessors are not so apt to leave descendants.

Somewhat puzzling is polydactylism—having extra fingers and toes like the boy opposite. It seems the work of a dominant gene and since there is no actual disadvantage involved, the question arises: why, over many generations, don't we all have six fingers? Is this a new mutation just beginning to work its way into the species, or is it linked to other, more harmful genes which hold it in check? Neither, say geneticists. The answer apparently lies partly in natural selection and partly in sexual selection: five-fingered people prefer five-fingered people for their mates, and polydactylism continues to be very rare. However it is common in cats, which often have six, and even seven toes, and don't seem to mind at all.

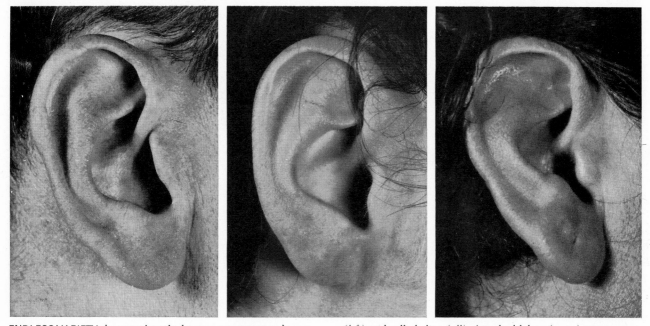

ENDLESS VARIETY characterizes the human ear; everyone's ears are unique. Some ear traits are inherited through dominant genes. Among them are free ear lobes, unattached to the head (*left*) and rolled rims (*all*). Attached lobes (*center*) are a recessive character. Rarely there appears on one ear a small cavity (*right*) that looks as if the ear has been pierced for an earring.

Of Giants and Dwarfs

Both dwarfism and giantism are caused by genetic peculiarities. Both conditions have sometimes affected whole races—like the Pygmies of Africa, who average four feet six inches in height, and the neighboring Watutsi, who average six feet six inches.

Scientists distinguish two kinds of dwarfs and giants. When the latter grow to eight feet or more, the condition is believed caused by an overactive pituitary gland, not by defective genes. It nearly always results in early death. Under eight feet it is probably a product of nonlethal, tall-stature genes. Occasionally both influences may be at work. The opposite of the genetic giant is the achondroplastic dwarf (*below*), characterized by near-normal torso and head with undersized limbs. The midget (*opposite*) is created by a genetically defective pituitary gland. Midgets have such childlike features as facial chubbiness but are well-proportioned miniatures of normal people and often live to ripe old ages.

TOO TALL FOR THE DOORWAY, eight-foot-two-inch Johann Petursson is actually only a medium-sized giant. His size may be the result of deficiencies that are more glandular than genetic.

BROTHER AND SISTER DWARFS of the Owitch family, successive products of a single dominant gene, come from dwarf parents. The gene rarely seems to impair fertility in its possessors.

BROTHER AND SISTER MIDGETS, the Del Rios celebrate their first Communion. Products of a genetic glandular fault, midgets often have normal parents but may be infertile themselves.

Appendix

A Comparison of Apes and Man

The resemblances and differences between man and the closest of his living relatives, the four great apes, are shown in the drawings and table below. The sketches of the body have been drawn to scale, and have been depicted here with all hair removed for unobscured comparison of the contours of the head and body.

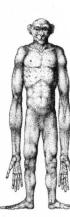 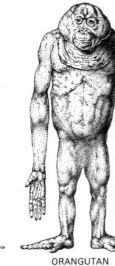 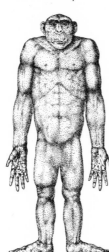 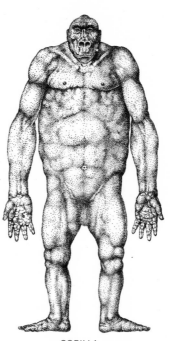 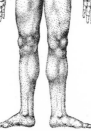

	GIBBON *Hylobates*	ORANGUTAN *Pongo pygmaeus*	CHIMPANZEE *Pan troglodytes*	GORILLA *Gorilla gorilla*	MAN *Homo sapiens*
NUMBER OF SPECIES	4 species 15 subspecies	1 species 2 subspecies	1 species 1 subspecies	1 species 2 subspecies	1 species 5 races
AVERAGE HEIGHT	2.3 ft.	4.9 ft. (male) 3.6 ft. (female)	5.6 ft. (male) 4.3 ft. (female)	5.9 ft. (male) 4.9 ft. (female)	5.6 to 5.8 ft. (male) 4.11 to 5.3 ft. (female)
AVERAGE WEIGHT	11 to 15 lbs.	110 to 165 lbs.	110 to 165 lbs.	250 to 550 lbs.	146 to 158 lbs. (male) 107 to 126 lbs. (female)
SOCIAL UNIT	Family bands of 20 to 30. Most gregarious of the apes	Small family bands. Least gregarious; males may live alone	Family bands of about six; may join with other bands. Fairly gregarious	Family bands. More gregarious than chimpanzees	Families, clans, tribes, sovereign states
DIET & FOOD HABITS	Mostly leaves, grass and fruits; also insects, snails, frogs, young birds' eggs	Predominantly fruit eaters; some leaves and bark	Essentially vegetarian; fruits, leaves, shoots, buds	Completely vegetarian; young leaves, berries, bark, roots, grains, fruits	Omnivorous
CRANIAL CAPACITY	5.95 to 7.60 cu. in.	23.5 to 25.0 cu. in.	23.1 to 27.0 cu. in.	27.9 to 32.5 cu. in.	61 to 113 cu. in.
AGE AT SEXUAL MATURITY	7 to 10 years	10 to 12 years	7 to 10 years	7 to 12 years	10 to 17 years
GESTATION PERIOD	200 to 212 days	270 days	202 to 261 days (231 average)	257 days	280 days
AVERAGE LONGEVITY	30 years*	30 years*	35 years*	50 years*	69.7 years (American)
ESTIMATED POPULATION	200,000+	2,500	100,000	25,000	3,100,000,000

* Based on animals in captivity

Bibliography

Classic Works on Evolution

Darwin, Charles, *Coral Reefs, Volcanic Islands, South American Geology.* Ward, Lock, London, 1874. Lady Nora Barlow, ed., *The Diary of the Voyage of H.M.S. Beagle.* Cambridge University Press, London, 1933. *The Different Forms of Flowers on Plants of the Same Species.* D. Appleton, New York and London, 1884 reprint. *Journal of Researches into the Geology and Natural History of the Various Countries Visited by H.M.S. Beagle (1839).* Hafner, New York and London, 1952. *The Origin of Species and the Descent of Man.* Modern Library, 1936. *Variations of Animals and Plants under Domestication* (2 vols.). Orange Judd, 1868. *The Various Contrivances by Which Orchids are Fertilized by Insects* (2nd ed.). John Murray, London, 1862. **The Voyage of the Beagle.* E. P. Dutton, 1950.

Darwin, Charles, and Alfred R. Wallace, *Evolution by Natural Selection.* Cambridge University Press, London, 1958.

Darwin, Francis, ed., *The Life and Letters of Charles Darwin* (2 vols.). Basic Books, 1959.

Darwin, Francis, and A. C. Seward, eds., *More Letters of Charles Darwin* (2 vols.). John Murray, London, 1903.

De Vries, Hugo, *The Mutation Theory* (Vols. I and II). Open Court Publishing Company, 1909. *Species and Varieties.* Open Court Publishing Company, 1905.

Fisher, Sir Ronald Aylmer, *The Genetical Theory of Natural Selection.* Clarendon Press, Oxford, 1930.

Haldane, J.B.S., *The Causes of Evolution.* Harper & Brothers, 1932.

Lamarck, Jean-Baptiste Pierre Antoine de Monet, Chevalier de, *Philosophie Zoologique* (Paris, 1809). Hafner, 1960.

Morgan, Thomas Hunt, *Evolution and Adaptation.* Macmillan, New York and London, 1903. *The Mechanism of Mendelian Heredity.* Henry Holt, 1933. *The Physical Basis of Heredity.* J. B. Lippincott, 1919.

Wallace, Alfred Russel, *My Life: A Record of Events and Opinions* (2 vols.). Dodd, 1905.

Fossils and Geology

Colbert, Edwin H., *Dinosaurs.* E. P. Dutton, 1961. **Evolution of the Vertebrates.* John Wiley & Sons, 1958.

Dunbar, Carl O., *Historical Geology* (2nd ed.). John Wiley & Sons, 1960.

Fenton, Carroll Lane, and Mildred Adams Fenton, *Fossil Book.* Doubleday, 1958.

*Matthews, William H., *Fossils.* Barnes & Noble, 1962.

Romer, Alfred S., *Vertebrate Paleontology* (2nd ed.). University of Chicago Press, 1945.

Evolution of Man

Andrews, Roy Chapman, *Meet Your Ancestors.* Viking Press, 1961.

Broom, Dr. Robert, *Finding the Missing Link.* C. A. Watts, London, 1950.

Clark, W. E. Le Gros, *The Fossil Evidence for Human Evolution.* University of Chicago Press, 1955.

Coon, Carleton S., *The Origin of Races.* Alfred A. Knopf, 1962. *The Seven Caves.* Alfred A. Knopf, 1957. *The Story of Man* (2nd ed.). Alfred A. Knopf, 1962.

*Dart, Raymond A., *Adventures with the Missing Link.* Harper & Brothers, 1959.

Dobzhansky, Theodosius, *Mankind Evolving.* Yale University Press, 1962.

Hooton, Ernest A., *Up From the Ape* (rev. ed.). Macmillan, 1946.

Howells, William W., *Mankind in the Making.* Doubleday, 1959.

*Leakey, Louis S. B., *Adam's Ancestors.* Harper & Brothers, 1960.

Moore, Ruth, *Man, Time, and Fossils.* Alfred A. Knopf, 1961.

*Oakley, Kenneth Page, *Man, the Tool Maker* (3rd ed.). British Museum (Natural History), 1956.

*Simpson, George Gaylord, *Life of the Past.* Yale University Press, 1961.

Von Koenigswald, G.H.R., *Meeting Prehistoric Man.* Harper & Brothers, 1957.

Weidenreich, Franz, *Apes, Giants and Man.* University of Chicago Press, 1946.

Genetics and Heredity

Anfinsen, Christian B., *The Molecular Basis of Evolution.* John Wiley & Sons, 1960.

Auerbach, Charlotte, *The Science of Genetics.* Harper & Brothers, 1961.

Bateson, W., *Mendel's Principles of Heredity.* Cambridge University Press, London, 1909.

Dobzhansky, Theodosius, *Evolution, Genetics and Man.* John Wiley & Sons, 1955. *Genetics and The Origin of Species* (3rd ed.). Columbia University Press, 1951.

Hutchins, Carleen Maley, *Life's Key—DNA.* Coward-McCann, 1961.

McLeish, John, and Brian Snoad, *Looking at Chromosomes.* Macmillan, 1959.

Muller, Hermann J., *Genetics, Medicine and Men.* Cornell University Press, 1947.

Sinnott, Edmund W., L. C. Dunn and Theodosius Dobzhansky, *Principles of Genetics.* McGraw-Hill, 1950.

Stern, Curt, *Principles of Human Genetics* (2nd ed.). W. H. Freeman, 1960.

Wallace, Bruce, and Theodosius Dobzhansky, *Radiation, Genes and Man.* Henry Holt, 1959.

General

Barclay, William Singer, *Land of Magellan.* Brentano's, 1927.

Barnett, Lincoln, and The Editors of LIFE, *The Wonders of Life on Earth.* Time Inc., 1960.

Beebe, William, *Galápagos, World's End.* G. P. Putnam's Sons, 1924.

Berrill, Norman John, *Journey into Wonder.* Dodd, Mead, 1952.

†Blum, Harold F., *Time's Arrow and Evolution.* Harper & Brothers, 1962.

Boulenger, Edward G., *Apes and Monkeys.* Robert M. McBridge, 1962.

Bridges, E. Lucas, *Uttermost Part of the Earth.* E. P. Dutton, 1949.

*Cain, A. J., *Animal Species and Their Evolution.* Harper & Brothers, 1960.

Eibl-Eibesfeldt, Irenäus, *Galápagos: The Noah's Ark of the Pacific.* Doubleday, 1961.

Eiseley, Loren, *Darwin's Century.* Doubleday, 1961.

Gregory, William King, *Evolution Emerging.* Macmillan, 1951.

Hutchins, Ross E., *Strange Plants and Their Ways.* Rand McNally, 1958.

Huxley, Sir Julian, *Evolution in Action.* Harper & Brothers, 1953. *Evolution—The Modern Synthesis.* Harper & Brothers, 1942.

Huxley, Thomas H., *Man's Place in Nature and Other Essays.* Everyman's Library, J. M. Dent & Sons, 1943.

*Irvine, William, *Apes, Angels, and Victorians.* McGraw-Hill, 1955.

*Lack, David, *Darwin's Finches.* Harper & Brothers, 1961.

Laver, James, *Victorian Vista.* Houghton Mifflin, 1955.

Libby, Willard F., *Radiocarbon Dating.* University of Chicago Press, 1952.

Lloyd, Francis E., *The Carnivorous Plants.* Chronica Botanica Company, Waltham, Mass., 1942.

Moore, Ruth, *Charles Darwin: A Great Life in Brief.* Alfred A. Knopf, 1955. *The Coil of Life.* Alfred A. Knopf, 1961.

*Romer, Alfred S., *Man and the Vertebrates* (2 vols.). University of Chicago Press, 1933.

*Simpson, George Gaylord, *The Meaning of Evolution.* Yale University Press, 1949.

Tax, Sol, ed., *Evolution After Darwin* (Darwin Centennial). Vol. I, *The Evolution of Life.* Vol. II, *The Evolution of Man.* Vol. III, *Issues in Evolution.* University of Chicago Press, 1960.

*Teilhard de Chardin, Pierre, *The Phenomenon of Man.* Harper & Brothers, 1959.

* Also available in paperback edition.

† Only available in paperback edition.

Index

Numerals in italics indicate a photograph or painting of the subject mentioned.

Credits

The sources for the illustrations in this book are shown below. Credits for pictures from left to right are separated by commas, top to bottom by dashes.

Cover—Dr. Robert I. Bowman
8, 10, 11—Culver Pictures
12—Drawings by Bob Kuhn
14—Courtesy Commander J. Smyth, O.B.E., R.N. from original notebook by Conrad Martens made on the voyage of the *Beagle*
17—Dr. I. Eibl-Eibesfeldt
18, 19—Rudolf Freund—painting by Adolph E. Brotman, Dr. Robert I. Bowman
20, 21—Rudolf Freund, Dr. Robert I. Bowman
22—Rolf Blomberg except right Dr. Robert I. Bowman
23—Rudolf Freund
24, 25—Rudolf Freund except left Rolf Blomberg
26, 27—Dr. Robert I. Bowman
28—Dr. Robert I. Bowman, Dr. I. Eibl-Eibesfeldt—Rudolf Freund
29—Dr. Robert I. Bowman—Dr. I. Eibl-Eibesfeldt
30—Dr. Robert I. Bowman—paintings by Jean Zallinger
31—Dr. I. Eibl-Eibesfeldt
32—Colonel Charles Wellington Furlong—drawing by Adolph E. Brotman
33—Colonel Charles Wellington Furlong
34, 35—Professor Martin Gusinde except bottom left Colonel Charles Wellington Furlong
36—Reprinted from *Mission Scientifique du Cap Horn*, 1882-1883, Gauthier-Villars Editeurs, Paris
37—Colonel Charles Wellington Furlong—Mario Planet
38—Nina Leen
40—The Bettmann Archive
41—Brown Brothers—Culver Pictures
42, 43—Drawings by Bob Kuhn
45—Drawing by Matt Greene
47—Ylla from Rapho-Guillumette
48, 49—Eileen Darby from Graphic House, Jürg Klages from Black Star
50, 51—Dr. Bertil Kullenberg of Uppsala Zoological Institution
52, 53—Lilo Hess
54, 55—W. H. Hodge except right center and right bottom George Kalmbacher

56, 57—Norman Chaffer
58—Andreas Feininger
59—J. R. Eyerman—Ray E. Johnson, Eric Schaal
60, 61—David Potts except top right David Fleay
62, 63—Left Joe Scherschel; center W. Suschitzky; right Karl H. Maslowski
64—Dr. Ross E. Hutchins except top right W. H. Hodge courtesy Wards National Science Establishment, Inc.
65—W. H. Hodge courtesy Wards National Science Establishment, Inc.
66—Left Eric Schaal—A. E. Ellis—Thomas D. McAvoy—Larry Burrows; center Eric Schaal—John Zimmerman—Robert W. Kelley; right Don Stephens—Thomas D. McAvoy—Albert Fenn—Larry Burrows
68, 69—Brown Brothers
70, 71—Drawings by Matt Greene
73—Drawing by Joseph Leibow
75, 76, 77—Ansel Adams from Magnum
78, 79—Peter Stackpole
80, 81—Eric Schaal
82—John Launois from Black Star
83—Albert Fenn
84—Left John Launois from Black Star; right Otto Hagel—Philippe Halsman (2)
85—Philippe Halsman except top right Albert Fenn from Pix
86, 87—Chart by Edwin Megargee
88—J. Whang and Dr. J. H. Tjio Lep Niamd from National Institutes of Health
90—Culver Pictures
92, 93—Drawings by Gaetano Di Palma
94, 95—Drawings by Matt Greene
97—Jerome P. Miksche from Brookhaven National Laboratory, Upton, Long Island
98, 99—Paintings by Antonio Petruccelli
100—Drawing by Jack J. Kunz
101—Drawings by Jack J. Kunz except top left Henry H. Jones
102, 103—Paintings by George V. Kelvin
104, 105—Dr. Landrum Shettles

courtesy *American Journal of Obstetrics and Gynecology*
106, 107—Dr. Arnold H. Sparrow and Robert F. Smith—Brookhaven National Laboratory, Upton, Long Island
108—Larry Burrows
110—Drawings by Gaetano Di Palma
111—Drawings by Matt Greene
112, 113—Drawings by Nino Carbe
114, 115—Drawings by Matt Greene
117—Los Angeles County Museum
118—Mildred Adams Fenton
119—Courtesy The American Museum of Natural History except top left Mildred Adams Fenton; center Dr. F. M. Carpenter
120—Roland T. Bird courtesy The American Museum of Natural History—courtesy The American Museum of Natural History
121—National Park Service
122 through 127—From *Prehistoric Animals* by Professor J. Augusta and Z. Burian, published by Paul Hamlyn Limited
128—Barbara Harrisson
130, 131—Drawings by Gaetano Di Palma except bottom right drawing by Matt Greene
133—Drawings by Nino Carbe
134, 135—Drawings by Gaetano Di Palma
137—Elsbeth Siegrist
138, 139—*Institut pour la Recherche Scientifique en Afrique Centrale*
140, 141—Dr. Kortlandt, University of Amsterdam
142, 143—S. L. Washburn except top right European Picture Service
144—The Smithsonian Institution
147—Drawings by Edward Malsberg
148, 149—Drawings by Helen Speiden
150—Drawings by Matt Greene
153, 154, 155—Des Bartlett
156, 157—Dr. John T. Robinson, University of Wisconsin
158 through 163—Paintings by Maurice Wilson for B.B.C.

School Publications courtesy the Natural History Museum, London, copied by Derek Bayes
164—David Linton
166—Adolph E. Brotman after *History of Man* by Gustav Schenk, Chilton Book Company
168—Map by Matt Greene—map by Nino Carbe
169—Map by Matt Greene—map by Nino Carbe
173—Camera Press from Pix, Eliot Elisofon, Thomas D. McAvoy—Jane Goodale, Marshall Expedition Peabody Museum of Harvard University-Smithsonian Institution
174—von-Meiss-Teuffen from Pix, Dr. Carleton Coon, Paul Popper—John Dominis, Mark A. Binn, Dr. Carleton Coon—Eliot Elisofon (2), Dr. Harry W. Wright courtesy University Museum, University of Pennsylvania
175—Dr. Carleton Coon, David Douglas Duncan, Dr. Carleton Coon—Howard Sochurek, Lisa Larsen, Dr. Carleton Coon—Maitland A. Edey, Dr. Carleton Coon, Oxford-Capetown Anthropological Expedition
176—Professor Shinobu Ishihara courtesy Caspar Krueger Dory Company
177—Gernsheim Collection, London—chart by R. M. Chapin, Jr.
178—*Bildarchiv der Oesterreichischen Nationalbibliothek*, Culver Pictures—Official Australian Photo from Wide World Photos
179—*Bildarchiv der Oesterreichischen Nationalbibliothek*, The Bettmann Archive, *Bildarchiv der Oesterreichischen Nationalbibliothek*—Robert W. Kelley, Herbert Gehr
180—Gabriel Benzur
181—Dr. Victor A. McKusick, Professor of Medicine, Johns Hopkins University School of Medicine except bottom right Dr. Clyde Keeler, Medical Geneticist, Milledgeville State Hospital
182—United Press International
183—Rice Studios L.T.D.
184, 185—Drawings by Ed Kasper

Acknowledgments

The editors of this book are particularly indebted to the following persons and institutions: Carleton S. Coon, Professor of Anthropology, University of Pennsylvania, and the late Francis J. Ryan, Professor of Zoology, Columbia University, who read the entire book and criticized the chapters in their own areas of study. The editors are also indebted to Harry L. Shapiro, Chairman and Curator, Physical Anthropology, and Charles M. Bogert, Chairman and Curator, Herpetology, American Museum of Natural History; Colonel Charles Wellington Furlong; Mrs. Evelyn Stefansson and the Stefansson Collection, Dartmouth College; Dr. Robert I. Bowman, San Francisco State College; the Horticultural Society of New York; Eric Holtzman and A. Mourad, Columbia University; and Glenn Jepsen, Professor of Geology, Princeton University.

Production Staff for Time Incorporated

Arthur R. Murphy Jr. (Vice President and Director of Production), Robert E. Foy, James P. Menton, Caroline Ferri and Robert E. Fraser

Text photocomposed under the direction of Albert J. Dunn and Arthur J. Dunn

xx

Printed by R. R. Donnelley & Sons Company, Crawfordsville, Indiana,
and by Livermore and Knight Co., a division of Printing Corporation of America, Providence, Rhode Island
Bound by R. R. Donnelley & Sons Company, Crawfordsville, Indiana
Paper by The Mead Corporation, Dayton, Ohio
Cover stock by The Plastic Coating Corporation, Holyoke, Massachusetts